Chemistry Calculations

Chemistry Calculations:

with a focus on algebraic principles

Alexander Vavoulis

Assistant Professor of Chemistry
California State College at Fresno

Holden-Day, Inc.

San Francisco, London, Amsterdam
1966

PREFACE

This book is intended for any beginning chemistry student who has difficulty in applying algebra to chemistry problems. This difficulty may arise for any number of reasons: The student may (1) have forgotten the algebra he previously learned, (2) never have learned the algebra adequately, or (3) not possess the ability to transfer his knowledge of algebra to the chemistry problems.

The student who requires a review of algebra will find this book helpful. All the topics of algebra which find application in beginning chemistry courses are given special attention. One important feature of this book is the integration of the chemistry and the algebra. Great concern is given to relating one to the other as simply and clearly as possible. A typical chapter includes a discussion of an algebraic topic, its application to chemistry, algebraic exercises, and typical chemistry problems. This intimate mixing of the two subjects will help the student effectively transfer the algebra to chemistry.

The algebra and chemistry exercises are graded; if used in a course the instructor can assign problems according to the ability level of the student. The book is indexed according to subjects in algebra and chemistry. A chemistry subject may be found in several places in the book because it may illustrate more than one algebraic principle. Charles' Law, for example, is found in Chapter 1, Axioms of Algebra, and in Chapter 7, Rectangular Coordinates.

The main objective of this book is not to teach the student all the chemistry he must know in a beginning course, but is to show clearly the application of algebra to chemical problems. The book, therefore, is supplementary to a chemistry text book and cannot be effectively used otherwise. For example, the Nernst Equation in Chapter 13 can only be given a superficial treatment for it is expected that the student will have his chemistry text available. A more extensive treatment of the many chemistry topics would, I believe, obscure the integration that is desirable.

Preface

I wish to acknowledge Dr. Floyd F. Helton, Chairman of the Mathematics Department, University of the Pacific. He gave assistance generously in the preliminary writing of this book. Also, my thanks go to Miss Celia Maldonado, who did a fine job of typing the various stages of the manuscript.

A. Vavoulis

TABLE OF CONTENTS

1. Axioms of Algebra

1.1	Introduction	1
1.2	Axioms	1
1.3	Application to Chemistry	2
	1. Dalton's Law of Partial Pressure	2
	2. Boyle's Law	2
	3. Heat	3
1.4	Algebra Problems	3
1.5	Chemistry Problems	4

2. Signed Numbers

2.1	Geometrical Consideration	5
2.2	Rules for Addition	5
2.3	Rules for Subtraction	6
2.4	Rules for Multiplication and Division	6
2.5	Application to Chemistry	7
	1. Oxidation State	7
	2. Temperature	8
	3. Electrochemistry	8
2.6	Algebra Problems	9
2.7	Chemistry Problems	10

3. Fundamental Principle

3.1	Introduction	11
3.2	Chemical Application	13
	1. Density	13
	2. Moles	13
	3. Moles per Liter	14
	4. Gram Equivalents	14
	5. Normality	14
3.3	Arithmetic Problems	15

3.4	Algebra Problems	15
3.5	Chemistry Problems	16

4. Monomials
4.1	Introduction	17
4.2	Exponential Numbers	17
4.3	Manipulation of Exponential Numbers	18
4.4	Chemical Applications	18
	1. Avogadro's Number	18
	2. Collision of Molecules	19
	3. Conversion of Units	19
	4. Ionization, Hydrolysis and Solubility Product	19
4.5	Algebra Problems	21
4.6	Chemistry Problems	21

5. Factoring and Its Inversion
5.1	Introduction	23
5.2	Applications to Chemistry	24
	1. Heat	24
	2. Equilibrium	25
	3. Vapor Pressure of Solutions	26
5.3	Algebra Problems	26
5.4	Chemistry Problems	27

6. Equivalent Equations
6.1	Types of Equations in Algebra	29
6.2	Classification of Equations	29
6.3	Equivalent Equations	30
6.4	Applications to Chemistry	31
	1. Temperature Conversion	31
	2. Mole Relationships in Chemical Reactions	32
	3. Weight and Volume Relationships in Chemical Reactions	33
	4. Titrations	33
	5. Equilibrium Constant	34
6.5	Algebra Problems	34
6.6	Chemistry Problems	35

7. Rectangular Coordinates
7.1	Introduction	37
7.2	The Graph of a Linear Equation	38
7.3	The Slope of a Line	38

7.4	Applications to Chemistry	39
	1. Charles' Law	39
	2. Specific Heat vs Temperature	40
	3. Vapor Pressure of Liquids	41
	4. Kinetics	42
7.5	Algebra Problems	42
7.6	Chemistry Problems	42

8. Systems of Equations

8.1	Pair of Linear Equations	45
	1. Substitution Method	45
	2. Elimination Method	46
	3. Method of Determinants	46
8.2	Double-Notation Method	47
8.3	Type of System and Its Solution	49
8.4	Other Types of Systems	50
8.5	Applications to Chemistry	50
	1. Analysis of a Mixture of Metals	50
	2. Analysis of a Mixture of Soluble Salts	51
	3. Chemistry Mixing Problems	52
8.5	Algebra Problems	53
8.6	Chemistry Problems	54

9. Irrational Numbers

9.1	Introduction	56
9.2	Reductio Ad Absurdum	56
9.3	Square Roots	57
9.4	Applications to Chemistry	58
	1. Diffusion of Gases	58
	2. Formation of Precipitate	58
	3. Chemical Equilibrium	59
9.5	Algebra Problems	59
9.6	Chemistry Problems	59

10. The Quadratic Equation

10.1	Introduction	61
10.2	Applications to Chemistry	62
	1. Ionization Constant	62
	2. Hydrolysis Constant	64
	3. Equilibrium Constant (in Solution)	65
	4. Equilibrium Constant (Gaseous State)	66

10.3   Algebra Problems   68
10.4   Chemistry Problems   68

11. Functions and Graphs

11.1   Introduction   70
11.2   Functions   71
11.3   Graphing Functions   72
11.4   Applications to Chemistry   74
    1. Density   74
    2. Boyle's Law   75
    3. Freezing Point Depression   75
11.5   Algebra Problems   75
11.6   Chemistry Problems   77

12. Inequalities

12.1   Introduction   78
12.2   Quadratic Inequalities   79
12.3   Solving Quadratic Inequalities   80
12.4   Applications to Chemistry   82
    1. Solubility Product Constant   82
12.5   Algebra Problems   84
12.6   Chemistry Problems   85

13. Logarithms

13.1   Introduction   86
13.2   Finding the Characteristic of a Logarithm   86
13.3   Finding the Mantissa of a Logarithm   87
13.4   Finding the Logarithm of a Number   88
13.5   Finding the Logarithm of a Number with Four Significant
    Digits   88
13.6   Finding the Number Whose Logarithm is Given   89
13.7   Multiplication   90
13.8   Division   91
13.9   Powers   92
13.10 Applications to Chemistry   92
    1. Calculation of pH   92
    2. Calculation of H^+ knowing the pH   92
    3. Solubility Product Calculations   93
    4. The Nernst Equation   93
13.11 Algebra Problems   95
13.12 Chemistry Problems   96

14. Natural Logarithms
14.1	Introduction	97
14.2	The Logarithmic Curve	98
14.3	The Exponential Curve	99
14.4	Applications to Chemistry	100
	1. Radioactive Decay	100
	2. Arrhenius Equation	103
14.5	Algebra Problems	103
14.6	Chemistry Problems	104

15. Significant Figures
15.1	Scientific Measurement	106
15.2	Identifying Figures	107
15.3	Application to Addition and Subtraction	108
15.4	Application to Multiplication and Division	108
15.5	Rounding Numbers	108
15.6	Significant Figures and Exponential Notation	109
15.7	Summary	109
15.8	Problems	110

16. Solving Problems
16.1	The Value of Algebraic Notation in Physics and Chemistry	111
16.2	Applications to Chemistry	111
16.3	Density	111
16.4	Charles' Law	112
16.5	Other Types of Problems and Their Solution	112
16.6	Problems	114

Appendix I
1.	Greek Alphabet	117
2.	Common Abbreviations	117
3.	Physical-Chemical Constants	117
4.	Metric Units and Conversion Factors	118
5.	Atomic Weights	118

Appendix II
1.	Vapor Pressure of Water	120
2.	Ionization Constants of Weak Electrolytes	121
3.	Dissociation Constants of Complex Ions	122
4.	Solubility Product Constants	123
5.	Oxidation-Reduction Potentials	124

Appendix III

1.	Logarithms	126
2.	Antilogarithms	128
3.	Answers to Even-Numbered Problems	130

Index

137

Chapter 1

Axioms of Algebra

1.1. Introduction

In algebra it is common to symbolize quantities by letters. Generally, these are letters from the English and Greek alphabets. For example, the letter l may correspond to any length of string, $2n$ corresponds to the multiplication of 2 by any numerical value of n, and $a + b$ means that the number represented by a is added to the number represented by b. It is seen that the letters exalt the quantity with a generalization unobtainable with specific numerical values.

1.2. Axioms

In a purely mathematical notation the axioms or fundamental laws of algebra may be written as follows:

$$a + b = b + a \qquad \text{Commutative Law of Addition}$$
$$ab = ba \qquad \text{Commutative Law of Multiplication}$$
$$a + (b + c) = (a + b) + c \qquad \text{Associative Law of Addition}$$
$$a(bc) = (ab)c \qquad \text{Associative Law of Multiplication}$$
$$a(b + c) = ab + ac \qquad \text{Distributive Law.}$$

The student may recall that these axioms are the same axioms used in arithmetic except that in arithmetic numbers are used rather than letters. The axioms of arithmetic are often written as follows:

$$1 + 2 = 2 + 1 \qquad \text{Commutative Law of Addition}$$
$$1(2) = 2(1)^* \qquad \text{Commutative Law of Multiplication}$$

* The parentheses as used in this example indicate multiplication.

1

$$1 + (2 + 3) = (1 + 2) + 3*$$ Associative Law of Addition
$$1(2 + 3) = (1 + 2)3$$ Associative Law of Multiplication
$$1(2 + 3) = 1(2) + 1(3)$$ Distributive Law.

1.3. *Application to Chemistry*

1. *Dalton's Law of Partial Pressures*

Dalton's Law of Partial Pressures exemplifies the associative law of addition. The law states that the total pressure of a mixture of gases in a closed container is the sum of the individual pressures. In algebraic form this would be

$$P_{total} = P_a + P_b + P_c + \cdots$$

if the container was filled with three gases designated as a, b, and c and their individual pressures designated as P_a, P_b, and P_c. For example, air consists mainly of nitrogen (78.03%), oxygen (20.99%), and argon (0.94%). (There are other gases in the air but these constitute the major proportion and will serve to illustrate the point.) When we have an automobile tire filled with air at a pressure of 30 lb. per sq. in. this pressure is a result of the individual pressures of the above three gases. The total pressure would be given by

$$P_{total} = P_{N_2} + P_{O_2} + P_{Ar},$$

where N_2, O_2, and Ar are the chemical symbols for nitrogen, oxygen, and argon, respectively. According to the associative law of addition it would not matter whether we first added the pressures of nitrogen and oxygen and then argon or the pressures of oxygen and argon and then nitrogen. The same numerical answer would be obtained.

2. *Boyle's Law*

Boyle's Law states that the product of the pressure and volume of a sample of a gas at some specified temperature is a constant. That is, $PV = k$. This simple equation can illustrate the commutative law of multiplication since it could have been written as $VP = k$. The equation is used, though, to compare the pressure and volume of a sample of gas at a different pressure and volume so that

---

* The parentheses as used in this example indicate how the numbers may be grouped differently without changing the answer.

$$\text{(initial)} \quad P_1 V_1 = P_2 V_2 \quad \text{(final)}$$

and $T = $ constant.

The equation could have been written as $V_1 P_1 = V_2 P_2$ or $V_1 P_1 = P_2 V_2$. (Another aspect of Boyle's Law is given in Section 11.4, Pt. 2.)

3. *Heat*

There is a change of temperature when, for example, ice is mixed with water. The change will depend upon the amount of ice and water, the temperature of both before mixing, and the specific heat of water. (Specific heat is the heat necessary to increase the temperature of a substance by one degree. This property changes as the temperature of the substance changes. For example, the specific heat of water is one because one calorie of heat is required to raise water through a one degree change. But the specific heat of ice is 0.5 because one-half a calorie raises the ice through a one degree change.) The heat gained or lost is given by

$$\text{Heat} = (\text{mass} \times \text{specific heat})(\text{temperature change})$$

which may also be written as

$$\text{Heat} = (\text{mass})(\text{specific heat} \times \text{temperature change}).$$

The above illustrates the associative law of multiplication.

1.4. *Algebra Problems*

State which axiom is illustrated in the following problems, and where numbers are present, evaluate the numbers on each side to show that an equality exists.

1. $6 + 2 = 2 + 6$
2. $15 + 6 = 6 + 15$
3. $(3 + 2) + 7 = 3 + (2 + 7)$
4. $(18 + 3) + 13 = 18 + (3 + 13)$
5. $2 \times (2 + 1) = 2 \times 2 + 2 \times 1$
6. $5 \times (3 + 4) = 5 \times 3 + 5 \times 4$
7. $3 \times (5 \times 2) = (3 \times 5) \times 2$
8. $8(3 \times 6) = (8 \times 3)6$
9. $(3 + 10) \times 5 = 3 \times 5 + 10 \times 5$
10. $(4 + 6)10 = 4 \times 10 + 6 \times 10$
11. $2 + (3 + 4) = (2 + 3) + 4$
12. $7 + (3 + 9) = (7 + 3) + 9$
13. $(2 \times 3) \times 4 = 2 \times (3 \times 4)$
14. $(7 \times 3) \times 5 = 7 \times (3 \times 5)$
15. $(2 \times 3) + 7 = 7 + (2 \times 3)$
16. $(p + q) + r = p + (q + r)$
17. $(a + b) + c = a + (b + c)$
18. $m + n = n + m$
19. $x + y = y + x$
20. $8(x + y) = 8x + 8y$
21. $x(y + f) = xy + xf$
22. $mn = nm$
23. $(m + n)(o + p) = (m + n)o + (m + n)p$
24. $x \cdot (y \cdot f) = (x \cdot y) \cdot f$
25. $abcd = adcb$

1.5. *Chemistry Problems*

In the following problems state which axiom is illustrated by the two equalities.

1. $P = h \times d$ and $P = d \times h$

2. $P_2 = P_1 \times \dfrac{V_1}{V_2} \times \dfrac{T_2}{T_1}$ and $P_2 = P_1 \times \dfrac{T_2}{T_1} \times \dfrac{V_1}{V_2}$

3. $P = P_{N_2} + P_{O_2} + P_{CO_2}$ and $P = P_{O_2} + P_{CO_2} + P_{N_2}$
4. $PV = n(RT)$ and $PV = (nR)T$
5. $M_{H_2SO_4} = 2H + S + 4O$ and $M_{H_2SO_4} = 4O + 2H + S$ (M = molecular weight)
6. $^{\circ}C = \frac{5}{9}(^{\circ}F - 32)$ and $^{\circ}C = \frac{5}{9}(^{\circ}F) - \frac{5}{9}(32)$
7. 50.000 gm $+ 0.060$ gm $+ 0.007$ gm $= 0.060$ gm $+ 0.007$ gm $+ 50.000$ gm
8. $P_1T_2 = P_2T_1$ and $T_2P_1 = T_1P_2$
9. $PV = kT$ and $VP = Tk$
10. $n = PV/RT$ and $n = VP/TR$

11. grams of solute $= M \times V \times \dfrac{\text{grams}}{\text{moles}}$ and

    grams of solute $= \dfrac{\text{grams}}{\text{moles}} \times V \times M$

    (where M = molarity, V = volume in liters)
12. coulombs = amperes $\times$ seconds and coulombs = seconds $\times$ amperes
13. $(N_{\text{acid}})(V_{\text{acid}}) = (N_{\text{base}})(V_{\text{base}})$,
    $(V_{\text{acid}})(N_{\text{acid}}) = (V_{\text{base}})(N_{\text{base}})$
14. Total moles in solution $= n(1 - \alpha + 2\alpha)$ and total moles in solution $= n - n\alpha + 2n\alpha$
15. pH + pOH = 14 and pOH + pH = 14

16. $K_i = \dfrac{[\text{H}^+][\text{OAc}^-]}{[\text{HOAc}]}$ and $K_i = \dfrac{[\text{OAc}^-][\text{H}^+]}{[\text{HOAc}]}$

17. $[\text{Ag}^+]^2[\text{CrO}_4^=] = 1 \times 10^{-12}$ and $[\text{CrO}_4^=][\text{Ag}^+]^2 = 1 \times 10^{-12}$

Chapter 2

Signed Numbers

2.1. Geometrical Consideration

Numbers which are assigned as positive or negative can be considered geometrically. That is, you draw a line as in Figure 2.1, select a point of

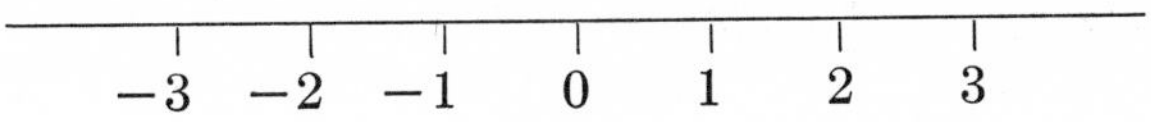

$$-3 \quad -2 \quad -1 \quad 0 \quad 1 \quad 2 \quad 3$$

FIGURE 2.1

origin, 0, and move in both directions numbering equidistant points. To the right the points are positive; to the left they are negative. If no sign is put in front of a number, it is assumed to be positive.

From geometrical considerations a positive number a has $-a$ as its reflection through the origin. The point -2, for example, is the same distance from the origin on the left side as the positive 2 is to the right on the other side. In general, then, $-(-a) = +a$ since $+a$ reflects $-a$ through 0.

The student should be aware that "$-a$" does not necessarily indicate a negative number. If, for example, $a = 2$ then $-a = -2$ and this is definitely a negative number. But if $a = -3$ then $-a = -(-3) = 3$.

2.2. Rules for Addition

1. For addition of two positive numbers the result is positive

$$(+2) + (+3) = +5.$$

2. For the addition of a positive and negative number of equal magnitude the result is zero

5

$$(-2) + (+2) = 0.$$

3. For the addition of two negative numbers the result is negative

$$(-2) + (-2) = -4.$$

4. For the addition of a positive and negative number of different magnitude the result is obtained by subtracting the smaller from the larger and prefixing the sign of the larger number

$$(-2) + (+3) = +1.$$

2.3. *Rules for Subtraction*

1. For the subtraction of two positive numbers of equal magnitude the result is zero

$$(+2) - (+2) = 0.$$

2. For the subtraction of two positive numbers of unequal magnitude $(a - b)$ change the sign of b and add

$$(+2) - (+3), \quad +2 - 3 = -1.$$

3. For the subtraction of two negative numbers of equal magnitude the result is zero

$$(-2) - (-2) = 0.$$

4. For the subtraction of two negative numbers of unequal magnitude $-a - (-b)$ change the sign of b and add

$$-2 - (-3), \quad -2 + 3 = +1.$$

2.4. *Rules for Multiplication and Division*

1. The product and quotient of two positive numbers are positive

$$(+2) \times (+3) = +6, \quad \frac{+4}{+2} = +2.$$

2. The product and quotient of two negative numbers are positive

$$(-2) \times (-3) = +6, \quad \frac{-4}{-2} = +2.$$

3. The product and quotient of a positive and negative number are negative

$$(-2) \times (+3) = -6, \quad \frac{-4}{+2} = -2.$$

4. The product of a positive number with zero is zero

$$(+2) \times 0 = 0$$

and the division of a number by zero is meaningless.

2.5. *Application to Chemistry*

1. *Oxidation State*

The oxidation state of an atom in a compound or ion is the arbitrary charge assigned to it according to a set of rules.

(a) The oxidation state of a free element is zero.
(b) The oxidation state of H is usually $+1$.
(c) The oxidation state of O is usually -2.
(d) In a compound the sum of the positive and negative oxidation states is zero.
(e) In an ion the sum of the positive and negative oxidation states is the charge of the ion.

The above rules, therefore, for handling positive and negative numbers find use in the determination of oxidation numbers.

Example 1. Find the oxidation number of P in H_3PO_4.

The sum of the positive and negative oxidation numbers must equal zero. Let P $= x$.

$$3(+1) + x + 4(-2) = 0$$
$$3 + x - 8 = 0$$
$$x - 5 = 0$$
$$x = +5.$$

Therefore, the oxidation number for P is $+5$.

Example 2. Find the oxidation number of Cr in $Cr_2O_7^{--}$.

The sum of the positive and negative oxidation numbers must equal -2. Let Cr $= x$.

$$2x + 7(-2) = -2$$
$$2x - 14 = -2$$

$$2x = -2 + 14$$
$$2x = +12$$
$$x = \frac{+12}{2} = +6.$$

Therefore, each Cr atom in the ion has an oxidation number of $+6$.

2. *Temperature*

Signed numbers occur in the conversion of one temperature to another. To convert °F to °C the following formula is used.

$$°C = \tfrac{5}{9} (°F - 32).$$

If the temperature reading is measured as $-30°F$, then

$$°C = \tfrac{5}{9} (-30 - 32).$$

Adding gives

$$°C = \tfrac{5}{9} (-62)$$

and multiplying gives

$$°C = -34.4.$$

To convert °C to °K it is necessary to add -34.4 to 273

$$°K = 273 + °C,$$
$$°K = 273 + (-34.4) = 238.6.$$

Signed numbers also occur in electrochemistry where it is desirable to determine the potential of a chemical reaction. The potential is useful because it indicates whether a certain reaction will occur under specified conditions.

3. *Electrochemistry*

Consider the following simple cell*

$$Zn|Zn^{++}(1\ M)|\ |Cu^{++}(1\ M)|Cu.$$

The half-cell reactions and their potentials (See Appendix II) are:

Left	$Zn \rightleftharpoons Zn^{++} + 2e$	$+0.762$ V
Right	$Cu \rightleftharpoons Cu^{++} + 2e$	-0.34 V.

---

* The single bar indicates a contact between two different phases, e.g., solid zinc and the zinc ion solution and solid copper and the copper ion solution.

The double bar indicates a salt bridge between the two solutions.

The overall reaction is obtained by subtracting the copper from the zinc half reaction. Therefore,

$$Zn - Cu \rightleftharpoons Zn^{++} - Cu^{++}$$

and the $2e$ cancel since $2e - 2e = 0$. Rearranging as with any algebraic equation we have

$$Zn + Cu^{++} \rightleftharpoons Zn^{++} + Cu.$$

The same operation is performed to obtain the voltage of the overall reaction.

$$0.762 - (-0.34)$$
$$0.762 + 0.34$$
$$1.102 \text{ V}$$

The positive value of 1.102 indicates that the reaction will occur as written, i.e., Zn will react with Cu^{++}. (Note: The student should observe that the answer in the above problem can be obtained by considering the two half reactions as they occur at the particular electrodes. For example, in the above cell:

Anode:	$Zn \rightleftharpoons Zn^{++} + 2e$	+0.762 V
Cathode:	$2e + Cu^{++} \rightleftharpoons Cu$	+0.34 V
Complete Cell:	$Zn + Cu^{++} \rightleftharpoons Zn^{++} + Cu$	+1.10 V.

(When a half reaction is reversed the numerical value of the voltage is changed.)

2.6. *Algebra Problems*

Perform the following additions:

1. $(-6) + (-5)$
2. $-8 + 9$
3. $(-3) + (-10)$
4. $-10 + 13$
5. $17 + (-3)$
6. $14 + (-9)$
7. $(-7) + (-5) + 7$
8. $(-10) + 3 + (-7)$
9. $(-6) + (-5) + (-4) + 3$
10. $(-10) + (-5) + 4 + 3$
11. $7 + 5 + 24 + (-33)$
12. $(-8) + (-8) + 22 + (-3)$

Perform the following subtractions:

13. $8 - 5$
14. $21 - 16$
15. $12 - (-16)$
16. $-5 - (-6)$
17. $-15 - (-15)$
18. $-7 - 9$
19. $5 - (-2) - (-8)$
20. $10 - (-3) - (-15)$
21. $(-4) - (-3) - (-5) - (-10)$
22. $(-5) - 3 - (-25) - (-30)$

Perform the following multiplications:

23. $(7)(8)$ 24. $7(-8)$ 25. $(-8)9$
26. $(-10)(-6)$ 27. $(-8)(-9)$ 28. $(-4)(-3)2$
29. $(-8)(-2)(-3)$ 30. $5(-6)(-3)$ 31. $4(-3)(-2)(-9)$
32. $7(-3)(-2)6$

Perform the following divisions:

33. $14 \div 7$ 34. $14 \div (-7)$ 35. $(-14) \div 2$
36. $(-30) \div (-5)$ 37. $(-72) \div (-9)$

Perform the following products and quotients:

38. $(3)(8) \div 6$ 39. $(-3)8 \div 6$
40. $(-6)(-9) \div (-27)$ 41. $(-12)(-16) \div (-8)(-6)$
42. $(-7)8 \div (8)(-3)$

2.7. Chemistry Problems

Using the equation for finding degrees Kelvin, $°K = °C + 273$, find $°K$ or $°C$.

1. $°C = 40$ 2. $°C = -32$ 3. $°C = -273$
4. $°K = 200$ 5. $°K = 432$ 6. $°K = 273$

Find degrees Centigrade for the following:

7. $°F = -32$ 8. $°F = +32$ 9. $°F = -52$
10. $°F = 152$ 11. $°F = 400$ 12. $°F = -100$

Using the table of electrode potentials in Appendix II determine the voltage of the overall reactions for the following half reactions:

13. $Cs - Cs^+$, $Fe - Fe^{++}$
14. $Cd - Cd^{++}$, $Cr^{+3} - Cr_2O_7^{--}(H^+)$
15. $I^- - I_2$, $Br^- - Br_2$
16. $Sn^{++} - Sn^{+4}$, $Mn^{++} - MnO_4^-(H^+)$
17. $Zn - Zn^{++}$, $MnO_2 - MnO_4^-(OH^-)$
18. $Cl^- - Cl_2$, $H_2O - H_2O_2(H^+)$

In the following half reactions find the overall reaction, the voltage and indicate whether the reaction will occur as written.

19. $H_2 - H_2O(H^+)$, $NO - NO_3^-(H^+)$
20. $Cl^- - Cl_2$, $Br^- - Br_2$
21. $Ag - AgCl$, $I^- - I_2$
22. $Co - Co^{++}$, $Li - Li^+$

Chapter 3

Fundamental Principle

3.1. Introduction

Basically, the solution of algebraic equations involves the manipulation of fractions. The student is familiar with the manipulation of arithmetical fractions. But before the transition from these to algebraic fractions is made, let us examine more closely what we do when solving ordinary fractions. Solutions like

$$\frac{5}{8} + \frac{4}{6} + \frac{1}{12} = \frac{5(3) + 4(4) + 1(2)}{24} = \frac{15 + 16 + 2}{24} = \frac{33}{24}$$

$$\frac{\overset{2}{\cancel{8}}}{\underset{5}{\cancel{35}}} \times \frac{\overset{1}{\cancel{7}}}{\underset{3}{\cancel{12}}} = \frac{2}{15} \quad \text{and} \quad \frac{7}{5} \div \frac{14}{35} = \frac{\overset{1}{\cancel{7}}}{\underset{1}{\cancel{5}}} \times \frac{\overset{7}{\cancel{35}}}{\underset{2}{\cancel{14}}} = \frac{7}{2}$$

are purely mechanical. Let us consider what logical process lies behind the above manipulations. Each fraction is multiplied by a fraction that equals one in order to get the same value for each denominator. This rule is known as the *Fundamental Principle* and is stated as follows:

The value of any fraction (or number) is unchanged if it is multiplied by a fraction (or number) equal to one.

$$\frac{5}{8} \times \frac{3}{3} + \frac{4}{6} \times \frac{4}{4} + \frac{1}{12} \times \frac{2}{2}.$$

Continuing the solution of the above example, we can now write it as

$$\frac{5 \times 3}{8 \times 3} + \frac{4 \times 4}{6 \times 4} + \frac{1 \times 2}{12 \times 2}$$

and from the above we obtain

$$\frac{15}{24} + \frac{16}{24} + \frac{2}{24} = \frac{33}{24}.$$

The rules used in working with fractions can be summarized as follows:

(a) $\dfrac{a}{b} = \dfrac{ma}{mb}$ (b) $\dfrac{a}{b} + \dfrac{c}{d} = \dfrac{ad + bc}{bd}$ (c) $\dfrac{a}{c} + \dfrac{b}{c} = \dfrac{a + b}{c}$

(d) $\dfrac{a}{b} \times \dfrac{c}{d} = \dfrac{ac}{bd}$ $(m \neq 0,\, b \neq 0,\, d \neq 0).$

The above rules may also be applied to the simplification of algebraic fractions. Consider the simplification of the following subtraction:

$$\frac{a - 2}{5} - \frac{a - 3}{3}.$$

Step 1. Multiply each fraction by a fraction equal to one (Fundamental Principle)

$$\frac{a - 2}{5} \times \frac{3}{3} - \frac{a - 3}{3} \times \frac{5}{5}.$$

Step 2. Combine the fractions (Rule c)

$$\frac{3(a - 2)}{5 \times 3} - \frac{5(a - 3)}{3 \times 5}.$$

Step 3. Simplify

$$\frac{3(a - 2)}{15} - \frac{5(a - 3)}{15}.$$

Step 4. Subtract (Rule b)

$$\frac{3(a - 2) - 5(a - 3)}{15}.$$

Step 5. Remove parentheses

$$\frac{3a - 6 - 5a + 15}{15}.$$

Step 6. Simplify by gathering similar terms

$$\frac{9 - 2a}{15}.$$

The student should be aware that the manipulation of arithmetical fractions is essentially the same as the manipulation of algebraic fractions. The use of letters in the algebraic fractions gives the fraction a generality that does not exist in an arithmetical fraction. This is one important aspect of algebra —the use of letters rather than numbers.

3.2. *Chemical Application*

1. *Density*

Fractions are not often used in chemical calculations, but units of measurement are and they can be manipulated in much the same manner as numbers. The Fundamental Principle can be used with the density formula

$$\text{Density} = \text{Mass/Volume.}$$

If the density of a substance is 3 gm/ml and there are 21 gm of the substance, what is its volume?

$$V = \frac{21 \text{ gm}}{3 \text{ gm/ml}}.$$

Using rule a: $\quad V = \dfrac{21 \text{ gm} \times \dfrac{\text{ml}}{\text{gm}}}{\dfrac{3 \text{ gm}}{\text{ml}} \times \dfrac{\text{ml}}{\text{gm}}} = \dfrac{21 \text{ gm} \times \dfrac{\text{ml}}{\text{gm}}}{3} = \dfrac{21 \text{ ml}}{3}$

$$V = 7 \text{ ml.}$$

2. *Moles*

A common calculation is to find the number of moles (gram-formula weights) in a certain weight of a compound. For example, how many moles are there in 100 gm of $KClO_3$?

$$\text{moles} = \frac{100 \text{ gm}}{122.6 \; \dfrac{\text{gm}}{\text{gm-formula wt.}}}$$

Using rule (a):

$$\text{moles} = \frac{100 \text{ gm} \times \dfrac{\text{gm-formula wt.}}{\text{gm}}}{122.6 \; \dfrac{\text{gm}}{\text{gm-formula wt.}} \times \dfrac{\text{gm-formula wt.}}{\text{gm}}} = \frac{100}{122.6} \text{ gm-formula wt.}$$

$$\text{moles} = 0.816 \text{ gm-formula wt. of } KClO_3.$$

3. *Moles per Liter*

The solubility of lead sulfate at 25°C is 0.035 gram per liter. To obtain the concentration in moles per liter divide the solubility by the formula weight (303)

$$\frac{0.035 \text{ gm/l}}{303 \text{ gm/mole}} = 1.15 \times 10^{-4} \frac{\text{gm/l}}{\text{gm/mole}}.$$

For proper units multiply numerator and denominator by moles/gm

$$\frac{\dfrac{\text{gm}}{\text{l}}}{\dfrac{\text{gm}}{\text{mole}}} \times \frac{\dfrac{\text{mole}}{\text{gm}}}{\dfrac{\text{mole}}{\text{gm}}} = \frac{\text{gm}}{\text{l}} \times \frac{\text{mole}}{\text{gm}} = \frac{\text{mole}}{\text{liter}}.$$

Therefore, $1.15 \times 10^{-4} \dfrac{\text{mole}}{\text{liter}}$ or $1.15 \times 10^{-4}M$ (M = molarity).

4. *Gram Equivalents*

The number of gram-equivalents in 3.560 gm of $CaCO_3$ is obtained by dividing the number of grams by the equivalent weight of $CaCO_3$. Therefore,

$$\frac{3.560 \text{ gm}}{50.05 \text{ gm/gm-eq}} = 0.0712 \frac{\text{gm}}{\text{gm/gm-eq}}.$$

For the proper units multiply numerator and denominator by gm-eq/gm

$$\frac{0.0712 \text{ gm} \times \dfrac{\text{gm-eq}}{\text{gm}}}{\dfrac{\text{gm}}{\text{gm-eq}} \times \dfrac{\text{gm-eq}}{\text{gm}}} = 0.0712 \text{ gm-eq of } CaCO_3.$$

5. *Normality*

The equivalent weight of Ca^{++} is obtained by dividing its atomic weight by its valence

$$\frac{40.08}{2} = 20.04.$$

If there are 0.08 gm of Ca^{++} in a liter of solution, then the normality of the solution is given by

$$\frac{0.08 \text{ gm}}{20.04 \text{ gm/gm-eq}} = 0.0039 \frac{\text{gm}}{\text{gm/gm-eq}}.$$

Again, using the Fundamental Principle

$$\frac{0.0039 \text{ gm} \times \dfrac{\text{gm-eq}}{\text{gm}}}{\dfrac{\text{gm}}{\text{gm-eq}} \dfrac{\text{gm-eq}}{\text{gm}}} = 0.0039 \text{ gm-eq of Ca}^{++}$$

and because this amount of Ca^{++} is in a liter of solution the concentration is designated as 0.0039 Normal or just $0.0039N$.

3.3. Arithmetic Problems

Reduce the following fractions to lowest terms by use of the Fundamental Principle.

1. 2/8   2. 10/20   3. 175/25   4. 42/14
5. 72/12   6. 28/68   7. 3/7   8. 16/72

Perform the additions in the following by using the Fundamental Principle.

9. $\frac{7}{12} + \frac{1}{6} + \frac{3}{2}$ 10. $\frac{1}{2} + \frac{1}{8} + \frac{1}{3}$ 11. $\frac{5}{2} + \frac{7}{8} + 2$
12. $\frac{5}{12} + \frac{3}{8} + \frac{1}{6}$ 13. $5 + \frac{1}{4} + \frac{1}{3}$ 14. $3 + 2 + \frac{1}{8}$

Perform the indicated operations and obtain the answer in its simplest form. Use the rules given above and state which rule is used in each step.

15. $\frac{4}{5} \times \frac{4}{9}$ 16. $\frac{5}{3} \times \frac{4}{2} \cdot \frac{6}{5}$ 17. $\frac{2}{9} \div \frac{6}{7}$
18. $\frac{9}{13} \div \frac{3}{4}$ 19. $\frac{8}{9} \times 6$ 20. $\frac{5}{8} \div 4$
21. $\frac{3}{5} \div \frac{7}{25}$ 22. $\frac{16}{17} \div \frac{11}{9}$ 23. $(4 + \frac{7}{8}) \div \frac{1}{8}$
24. $\frac{2}{5}(\frac{1}{3} + \frac{1}{10})$ 25. $\frac{4}{4}(\frac{16}{9} + \frac{1}{4})$ 26. $16 \div (\frac{4}{3} + \frac{1}{4})$

3.4. Algebra Problems

Simplify the following algebraic fractions. Use the Fundamental Principle and the rules for fractions.

1. $\dfrac{3x}{4} - \dfrac{5x}{6} - \dfrac{x}{3}$ 2. $\dfrac{3x}{4} - \dfrac{4x}{7} - \dfrac{5x}{11}$ 3. $\dfrac{x+y}{3} + \dfrac{x-y}{7}$

4. $\dfrac{m+n}{4} - \dfrac{m+n}{3}$ 5. $\dfrac{2x-2}{6} + \dfrac{4x+1}{9}$ 6. $\dfrac{5x+3}{7} + \dfrac{2x-1}{3}$

7. $\dfrac{a}{b} \div \dfrac{c}{d}$ 8. $\dfrac{a}{b} \div c$ 9. $a \div \dfrac{b}{c}$

10. $\dfrac{x}{y} \div \dfrac{f}{w}$ 11. $x \div \dfrac{b}{x}$ 12. $a - \dfrac{1}{b} \div b - \dfrac{1}{a}$

13. $\dfrac{a}{x} + 1 \div \dfrac{b}{x} - 1$

3.5. *Chemistry Problems*

The following problems include practice in the use of rule (a). Rule (a) is also applied where measurement units are involved in the calculation.

1. How many inches are there in 100 cm?
2. How many millimeters are there in 13.8 cm?
3. Convert 1000 in.² to m².
4. Convert one cubic meter to liters.
5. How many kilograms in 132 lb.?
6. The wavelength of the yellow light from a sodium lamp is approximately 5.9×10^{-5} cm. What is this in Ångstrom units?
7. How many grams of sulfur are there in 88 lb. of sulfur?
8. What volume will 200 gm of mercury occupy?
9. The density of carbon tetrachloride is 1.60 grams per cubic centimeter. What volume does 20 gm occupy?
10. How many moles are there in 30 gm of C_6H_6?
11. How many moles are there in 50 gm of H_2SO_4?
12. How many moles of water do 6.69×10^{23} molecules of water represent?
13. Determine the molality of a solution which contains 10.0 grams of sugar, $C_{12}H_{22}O_{11}$, dissolved in 100 grams of water?
14. Calculate the molarity of a sulfuric acid solution of specific gravity 1.198 containing 27.0% H_2SO_4 by weight.
15. Determine the normality of a solution containing 8.12 gm of HNO_3 per liter of solution.
16. Calculate the volume of 4.0N solution which contains 2.24 gram equivalents.
17. In an oxidation-reduction reaction the equivalent weight of H_2S is 17.04. How many gram equivalents does 100 gm of H_2S represent?
18. If 22.4l of C_2H_4 (1 mole) at S.T.P. produces 337 kcal, how many kcal are produced by 1000 l?
19. How many gram-equivalent weights of hydrogen are there in 0.504 gm of hydrogen? (Equivalent weight of hydrogen = 1.008.)

Chapter 4

Monomials

4.1. *Introduction*

An algebraic expression is a combination of numbers (or letters) linked together by addition, subtraction, multiplication, and division or any combination of the four processes. Parts of such expressions separated by $+$ or $-$ signs are called *terms*. An expression of two or more terms is called a *polynomial*. Algebraic expressions can also be distinguished by a monomial, x^2, binomial, $a + b$, trinomial, $x^2 + y^2 + 3$, etc.

4.2. *Exponential Numbers*

A *power* of a quantity is the product obtained by multiplying that quantity by itself depending on the value of the power. The power is expressed by writing to the right and above the quantity an index which indicates the number of factors to be taken. For example,

$$x \times x \text{ is written as } x^2$$
and
$$x \times x \times x \text{ is written as } x^3, \text{ etc.}$$

The small number which expresses the power of any quantity is called an *exponent*. Thus, the exponent of y^5 is 5 and that of 5^3 is 3. The literal quantities (i.e., x) oftentimes have a numerical factor called the *coefficient*. The coefficient in the term $4x^3$ is 4 and if the coefficient of a quantity is not explicitly written, it is understood to be 1.

In science, often we deal with large or small numbers and represent them as powers of ten. That is, 700 000 000 is written as 7×10^8; 100 000 as 1×10^5; 0.00001 as 1×10^{-5}; 0.00000001 as 1×10^{-8}. The exponents of the last two values are negative and the coefficient 1 could have been omitted.

4.3. *Manipulation of Exponential Numbers*

The two numbers, 6000 and 200, written in exponential form are 6×10^3 and 2×10^2, respectively. They are multiplied as follows:

$$6 \times 10^3 \times 2 \times 10^2 = (6 \times 2)(10^3 \times 10^2),$$

and it is evident that the distributive law is being applied. Continuing the above we obtain

$$6 \times 2 = 12 \quad \text{and} \quad 10^3 \times 10^2 = 10^5$$

which, when combined, yields 12×10^5 or 1.2×10^6. (By convention an exponential number is written with one figure to the left of the decimal point.) The above was obtained in the following way:

$$10^3 = \underset{\text{3 factors}}{10 \times 10 \times 10} \qquad\qquad 10^2 = \underset{\text{2 factors}}{10 \times 10}$$

$$10^3 \times 10^2 = \underset{(3+2)\ \text{factors}}{(10 \times 10 \times 10) \times (10 \times 10)} = 10^5.$$

In general

$$10^n \times 10^m = 10^{n+m}.$$

If the two are divided, we get by a rule of fractions

$$\frac{6 \times 10^3}{2 \times 10^2} = \frac{6}{2} \times \frac{10^3}{10^2}, \quad \frac{10^3}{10^2} = \frac{\overset{\text{3 factors}}{10 \times 10 \times 10}}{\underset{\text{2 factors}}{10 \times 10}} = 10$$

and

$$\frac{6}{2} \times \frac{10^3}{10^2} = 3 \times 10 = 30.$$

In general

$$\frac{10^n}{10^m} = 10^{n-m}.$$

Let us summarize the various rules governing the use of exponents.

(a) $a^n a^m = a^{n+m}$ (b) $(ab)^n = a^n b^n$

(c) $a^n/a^m = a^{n-m}$ (d) $(a^m)^n = a^{mn}.$

4.4. *Chemical Applications*

1. *Avogadro's Number*

Avogadro's number, 6.02×10^{23}, is an important number which tells us, for example, how many oxygen molecules (O_2) are contained in 22.4 liters

(1.26 cu. ft.) at 0°C and atmospheric pressure (760 mm of Hg). This is true for any gas, and notice that the number is extremely large. To get some idea of its magnitude consider the following calculation. The area of Texas is close to 262 000 sq. miles. If it were covered with a layer of fine sand 50 feet thick and each grain of sand were $\frac{1}{100}$ of an inch in diameter, there would be Avogadro's number of particles of sand. It should be obvious that it would be inconvenient to write such a large number in any other way.

2. *Collision of Molecules*

If 1 mole oxygen (or any other gas) was at 0°C and 760 mm Hg pressure, then the number of collisions occurring between the molecules each second would be 4 000 000 000. The scientific notation for this number is 4×10^9.

3. *Conversion of Units*

Exponential numbers are often encountered in certain types of conversion problems. For example, let us calculate the number of cubic centimeters (cm³) in one cubic meter (m³)

$$
\begin{aligned}
1 \text{ m}^3 &= 1 \text{ m} \times 1 \text{ m} \times 1 \text{ m} \\
&= 100 \text{ cm} \times 100 \text{ cm} \times 100 \text{ cm} \\
&= 10^2 \text{ cm} \times 10^2 \text{ cm} \times 10^2 \text{ cm} \\
&= 10^6 \text{ cm}^3.*
\end{aligned}
$$

4. *Ionization, Hydrolysis, and Solubility Product*

(a) Calculate the present ionization of a 0.04 M solution of HCN whose hydrogen ion concentration is 4×10^{-6}.

Solution:

$$\text{Degree of ionization} = \frac{[H^+]\dagger}{[HCN]} = \frac{4 \times 10^{-6}}{4 \times 10^{-2}} = 1 \times 10^{-4}$$

$$\text{Percent ionization} = \frac{[H^+]}{[HCN]} \times 100$$

$$= 1 \times 10^{-4} \times 10^2 = 1 \times 10^{-2} = .01\%.$$

(b) Calculate the hydrogen ion concentration in a 0.002 M solution of HBrO. (K_i for HBrO is 2.0×10^{-9}.)

---

* This number should be written as 1×10^6. The one is often omitted but is understood to be there.
† The bracket always indicates moles/liter.

Solution:

$$HBrO \rightleftharpoons H^+ + BrO^-$$

$$K = \frac{[H^+][BrO^-]}{[HBrO]}$$

Let $x = [H^+] = [BrO^-]$.

$$2 \times 10^{-9} = \frac{x \times x}{2 \times 10^{-3} - x} = \frac{x^2}{2 \times 10^{-3}}.$$

(x is small as compared to 2×10^{-3}.)

$$(2 \times 10^{-9})(2 \times 10^{-3}) = x^2$$
$$(4 \times 10^{-12}) = x^2$$
$$2 \times 10^{-6} = x = [H^+].$$

(c) Calculate the copper ion concentration in a saturated solution of CuCNS. (K_{sp} for CuCNS is 4×10^{-14}.)

Solution:

$$CuCNS \rightleftharpoons Cu^+ + CNS^-$$
$$K_{sp} = [Cu^+][CNS^-]$$
Let $x = [Cu^+] = [CNS^-]$
$$4 \times 10^{-14} = x \cdot x = x^2$$
$$2 \times 10^{-7} = x = [Cu^+].$$

(d) Calculate the hydrolysis constant for cyanide ion.

Solution:

$$K_{CN^-} = \frac{K_W}{K_{HCN}} = \frac{1 \times 10^{-14}}{4.0 \times 10^{-10}}$$

$$K_{CN^-} = 0.25 \times 10^{-4}$$
$$\text{or } K_{CN^-} = 2.5 \times 10^{-5}.$$

(To shift the decimal point multiply 0.25 by 10 and divide 10^{-4} by 10.)

(e) Calculate the hydroxide ion concentration in a 0.04 M solution of NaCN. (K_h for CN$^-$ is 2.5×10^{-5}.)

Solution:

$$CN^- + H_2O \rightleftharpoons HCN + OH^-$$

$$K_h = \frac{[HCN][OH^-]}{[CN^-]}$$

Let $x = [OH^-] = [HCN]$

$$2.5 \times 10^{-5} = \frac{x^2}{4 \times 10^{-2}}$$

$$(4 \times 10^{-2})(2.5 \times 10^{-5}) = x^2$$
$$10.0 \times 10^{-7} = x^2$$
$$\text{or } 100 \times 10^{-8} = x^2$$
$$10 \times 10^{-4} = x = [\text{OH}^-]$$
$$\text{or } 1 \times 10^{-3} = [\text{OH}^-].$$

4.5. Algebra Problems

Write the following numbers as the product of two numbers one of which is an integral power of 10 and the other written with one digit to the left of the decimal point.

1. 22 400
2. 7 200 000
3. 454
4. 0.454
5. 0.0454
6. 0.00006
7. 0.00306
8. 0.0000005
9. 300

Write the following products without an integral power of 10.

10. 2×10^{-6}
11. 8×10^{-2}
12. 5.6×10^{-2}
13. 1.6×10^4
14. 3.5×10^{-6}
15. 4×10^8
16. 7×10^{-3}
17. 1.25×10^5
18. 125×10^3

Perform the indicated operations with the following:

19. $(8 \times 10^3)(2.5 \times 10^3)$
20. $(48 \times 10^6) \div (12 \times 10^2)$
21. $(7.8 \times 10^{-3}) \div (1.2 \times 10^2)$
22. $(4 \times 10^{-3})(5 \times 10^4)^2$
23. $(6\,000\,000)(0.00004)^4 \div (800)^2(0.002)^3$
24. $(2 \times 10^{-3})(9 \times 10^3)(4 \times 10^{-2})$ *0.72*
25. $(4 \times 10^{-1})(3 \times 10^3)(6 \times 10^{-2})$
26. $(1 \times 10^{-3})(2 \times 10^5)^2$
27. $(3 \times 10^2)^3(2 \times 10^{-5}) \div (3.6 \times 10^{-8})$
28. $8(2 \times 10^{-2})^{-2}$
29. $x^6 \div x^3$
30. $(x^2)^3$
31. $y^2 y^3$
32. $x^{17} \cdot x^{-3}$
33. $a^{-12} a^5$
34. $(b^{-2})^{-4}$
35. $c^{-2} \div c^{-4}$

4.6. Chemistry Problems

In doing the following problems the student ought to write numerical values in exponential form whenever possible. Conversion factors may be found in Appendix I.

1. How many milliliters are there in one cubic centimeter? *1 · 1 ml = 1 cm³*
2. How many liters are there in one cubic meter? *1×10³ l*
3. Convert the molar volume of 22.4 l to milliliters.
4. Convert 20 000 gm to kilograms. *20 kg*
5. Convert 100 000 l to milliliters.
6. The diameter of a molecule is 4Å. Express the diameter in centimeters and meters. (Å = Angstrom.)
7. What is the wavenumber ($\sigma = 1/\lambda$) of light of wavelength (λ) 4000 Å?
8. The wavelength, λ, is given by c/ν (ν = frequency of the light and c is the velocity

of light equal to 3×10^{10} cm/sec). Calculate the wavelength of light that has a frequency of 1×10^{12} vibrations per second.

9. How many molecules are there in 3 gm of water?
10. How many atoms of oxygen are there in 22 gm of carbon dioxide? (Use 44 for the molecular weight of carbon dioxide.)
11. How many moles of water are there in 6.02×10^{22} molecules of water?
12. It was found that the number of moles of Hg per cubic centimeter at $-120°C$ is 1×10^{-23}. How many atoms of Hg does this represent?
13. To how many moles of Sn do 5.36 atoms of Sn correspond?
14. What is the mass in grams of 2.23×10^{24} atoms of Cu?
15. It is found that 3.01×10^{22} molecules of an unknown gas have a mass of 3.00 gm. What is the molecular weight of the gas?
16. What is the hydroxide ion concentration in a solution whose hydrogen ion concentration is 1×10^{-6}? $[H^+][OH^-] = K_w = 1 \times 10^{-14}$.
17. What is the hydrogen ion concentration in a solution whose hydroxide ion concentration is 3×10^{-9}?
18. What is the hydrogen ion concentration in a 1 M solution of HCN?
19. What is the hydrogen ion concentration in a 0.005M solution of acetic acid? ($K_i = 1.76 \times 10^{-5}$.)
20. The molar solubility of calcium hydroxide is 1.26×10^{-2} moles/1. What is the solubility product constant for calcium hydroxide?

Chapter 5

Factoring

5.1. *Introduction*

To factor a number means to break it up into a product of two or more numbers. These two or more numbers are called *factors* and the determination of these numbers *factoring*.

The factors for the number 15 are 3 and 5 since $15 = 3 \times 5$. The numbers 3 and 5 are *prime* numbers because the factors of these numbers are the numbers themselves, i.e., 3 and 5 and the number one. That is,

$$3 = 3 \times 1$$

and

$$5 = 5 \times 1.$$

For the number 100 there are the factors 4 and 25 but its prime factors are 2, 2, 5, and 5. If the reverse of factoring is performed, i.e., if all prime factors are multiplied together, the original unfactored number is obtained. That is,

$$2 \times 2 \times 5 \times 5 = 100.$$

A polynomial,* an algebraic expression with two or more terms and one or more letters, may be factored. In attempting to factor a polynomial expression the student should look for a factor common to all the terms in the expression. The polynomial $15x + 10xy$ is, therefore, factored as

$$5(3x + 2xy)$$

and then

$$5x(3 + 2y).$$

* See Section 4.1.

It should be observed that the original expression is obtained if the two factors are multiplied together. A polynomial such as

$$au - av + aw - ax$$

is obviously factored as

$$a(u - v + w - x).$$

Four other common factorizations are the following:

$$(a + b)(a - b) = a^2 - b^2$$
$$(a + b)^2 = (a + b)(a + b) = a^2 + 2ab + b^2$$
$$(a - b)^2 = (a - b)(a - b) = a^2 - 2ab + b^2$$
$$(x + b)(x + d) = x^2 + (b + d)x + bd.$$

5.2. *Applications to Chemistry*

The inverse of factoring (multiplication) is encountered in chemical problems more often than factoring. Nevertheless, the student should understand factoring because it enhances his ability to manipulate certain chemical problems. The following examples are illustrative:

1. *Heat*

Determine the resulting temperature, t, when 150 gm of ice at 0°C are mixed with 400 gm of water at 40°C.

Solution:

Heat to melt ice = mass $\times$ heat of fusion = 150 gm $\times$ 80 cal/gm = 1.20 $\times$ 10⁴ cal

Heat to raise temperature of 150 gm of water at 0°C to final temperature = mass $\times$ specific heat $\times$ temperature change = 150 $\times$ 1 $\times$ $(t - 0)$ cal

Heat lost by 200 gm of water = mass $\times$ specific heat $\times$ temperature change = 400 $\times$ 1 $\times$ $(40 - t)$ cal

$$\text{Heat lost} = \text{Heat gained}$$
$$400(40 - t) = 12\,000 + 150t.$$

Simplify the left side by multiplying both factors together

$$16000 - 400t = 12000 + 150t$$
$$-400t - 150t = 12000 - 16000 = -4000$$
$$400t + 150t = 4000.*$$

* See Chapter 6.

Simplify by factoring the left side (or add)

$$(400 + 150)t = 4000$$
$$550t = 4000$$

$$t = \frac{4000}{550} = 7.3°C.$$

2. *Equilibrium*

How many moles of CO_2 are formed at equilibrium when CO_2 and graphite are reacted at 817°C and at a total pressure of 2 atm? $K_p = 10$. Let α = moles of CO_2 changed; then 2α is moles of CO produced

$$CO_{2(g)} + C_{(s)} \rightleftharpoons 2\ CO_{(g)}.$$

Moles of gas at equilibrium: $1 - \alpha$ 2α.

Total moles of gas: $1 - \alpha + 2\alpha = 1 + \alpha$

$$K_p = \frac{(P_{CO})^2}{P_{CO_2}}.$$

$$10 = \frac{\left(\dfrac{2\alpha}{1 + \alpha} P\right)^2}{\dfrac{1 - \alpha}{1 + \alpha} P}$$

$$10 = \frac{\dfrac{4\alpha^2}{(1 + \alpha)^2} P^2}{\dfrac{1 - \alpha}{1 + \alpha} P} = \frac{\dfrac{4\alpha^2}{(1 + \alpha)^2} (2)}{\dfrac{1 - \alpha}{1 + \alpha}} \quad \text{(since } P = 2 \text{ atm)}$$

$$10 = \frac{8\alpha^2}{(1 + \alpha)^2} \times \frac{1 + \alpha}{1 - \alpha}\ \text{*}$$

$$10 = \frac{8\alpha^2}{(1 + \alpha)(1 - \alpha)} = \frac{8\alpha^2}{1 - \alpha^2}$$

$$10(1 - \alpha^2) = 8\alpha^2$$
$$10 - 10\alpha^2 = 8\alpha^2$$
$$10 = 18\alpha^2$$
$$\tfrac{10}{18} = \tfrac{5}{9} = \alpha^2$$

$$\alpha = \sqrt{\frac{5}{9}} = \frac{\sqrt{5}}{3} = \frac{2.24}{3} = 0.75.$$

Therefore, at equilibrium there are $1 - 0.75 = 0.25$ moles of CO_2 unconverted.

* See Chapter 2.

3. *Vapor Pressure of Solutions*

The vapor pressure of a liquid decreases when a non-volatile solute is added to it, and the decrease depends upon the numbers of molecules of solute added. The vapor pressure of a solvent over a solution containing the solvent is a product of the vapor pressure of pure solvent and the mole fraction of solvent. The mole fraction of solvent is given by

$$\frac{\text{moles of solvent}}{\text{moles of solvent} + \text{moles of solute}}.$$

Example 1. Dissolving 10.0 gm of a non-volatile solute in 2.30 moles of benzene (liquid) at 21°C reduces the vapor pressure from 80.0 to 78.4 mm. Determine the molecular weight of the solute. Let x = molecular weight of solute

$$78.4 = (80.0)\,\frac{2.30}{2.30 + 10.0/x}$$

$$78.4 = (80.0)\,\frac{2.30x}{2.30x + 10.0} \qquad \text{(using the Fundamental Principle)}$$

$$78.4 = \frac{184x}{2.30x + 10.0}$$

$$78.4\,(2.30x + 10.0) = 184x$$
$$182x + 784 = 184x$$
$$784 = 2x$$
$$392 = x.$$

Therefore, the molecular weight of the solute is 392.

5.3. *Algebra Problems*

Obtain the prime factors of the following numbers:

1. 48	2. 28	3. 30
4. 200	5. 220	6. 365
7. 72	8. 284	9. 182

Factor the following polynomials:

10. $8a - 12$

11. $bx + by$

12. $3x - 4x$

13. $30x^2 + 5x - 10$

14. $mno - mo$

15. $bx + 2by + 3bz$

16. $21xy - 3x$

17. $x^3 + 2x^2 - x$

18. $a^2(a^2 - 3a + 5) - 7(a^2 - 3a + 5)$

19. $4(a + b) - 5(a + b)$

20. $x^2(a - b) + y^2(a - b) - 3(a - b)$

21. $7(c - 2d) - 4a(c - 2d)$

22. $3h(x - 2) - 4k(x - 2)$

23. $m^2(m - 3) - (3m + 2)(m - 3)$

24. $m^2 - n^2$

25. $4q^2 - p^2$ 26. $18y^2 - 8x^2$ 27. $4m^2 - 9n^2$

28. $49a^2 - 1$ 29. $1 - 81x^2y^2$ 30. $b(y^2 - x^2)$

31. $16a^2 - 4b^2$ 32. $2z^3 - 2zy^2$ 33. $b^2 - 16b^4$

34. $100b^2 - b^4$ 35. $m^4n^2 + r^6s^8$ 36. $(m + n)^2 - c^2$

37. $(x - 2)^2 - 36y^2$ 38. $(2x + y)^2 - 25z^2$

39. $(x + 3y)^2 - (z - 3y)^2$ 40. $(m + n)^2 - (o - p)^2$

41. $4(a - b)^2 - 1$ 42. $3(m - n)^2 - 27$

43. $4a^2(m + n) - 9b^2(m + n)$ 44. $m^3 - n^3$

45. $8c^3 - 27d^3$ 46. $a^3 - 125$

47. $27x^3 - 48y^3$ 48. $m^3(m - n)^3 + m^3$

49. $a^3b^6 - (ab - c^2)^3$

Carry out the following multiplications:

50. $2a(5b + 4x)$ 51. $2y(3x - 4w)$

52. $-5z(3x + 2y)$ 53. $-3z(2x^2 + 2x - 4)$

54. $2a(a^2 - 3a + 5)$ 55. $(x - 3)(x - 6)$

56. $(x - 3)(x + 4)$ 57. $(2a - 1)(4a - 5)$

58. $(3a - 2)(2a + 3)$ 59. $(a + 2)(a^2 + a + 4)$

60. $(x - 3)(x^2 - 3x + 4)$ 61. $(m + n)(m + n)$

62. $(m - n)(m + n)$ 63. $(m - n)(m^2 + mn + n^2)$

64. $(mx^a + n)(mx^a - n)$ 65. $(2x^2 - 2x - 3)(2x^2 - xy + 3y^2)$

66. $(3x^2 + x - 2)(3x^2 + 2xy - y^2)$

5.4. Chemistry Problems

1. The specific gravity of kerosene was determined to be 0.819. What is the weight of the specific gravity bottle used if it weighs 330 gm when filled with water and 301 gm when filled with kerosene? (specific gravity = mass of kerosene/mass of equal volume of water).

2. Express $-32°F$ in degrees Centigrade. $°C = \frac{5}{9}(°F - 32)$.

3. Express $440°F$ in degrees Centigrade.

4. How many grams of sugar would have to be dissolved in 70 gm of water to yield a 30% solution? (Let x = wt. of sugar. Weight of solution is the weight of sugar plus the weight of the water.)

5. A sample of gold (sp. gr. = 19.3) and quartz (sp. gr. = 2.7) weighs 50 gm. The specific gravity of the sample is 7.6 g/cm.^{3} How much gold and quartz is there in the sample? (Hint: Let x = wt. of gold and $50 - x$ = wt. of quartz. The volume of the sample equals the sum of the volumes of the gold and quartz.)

6. When 1 mole of ethanol (ethyl alcohol) at 25°C is mixed with 1 mole of acetic acid, the K_c value is 4. How many moles of ester are formed if 4 moles of alcohol are mixed with 1 mole of acid? See Section 10.2, 3.

7. The K_p for the reaction $N_2O_4{}_{(g)} \rightleftharpoons 2NO_2{}_{(g)}$ at 25°C is 0.14. What is the percent dissociation of 1 mole of N_2O_4 at 25°C and 1 atm pressure?

8. When 100 gm of ice at 0°C are mixed with 200 gm of water at 70°C, what is the final temperature of the mixture?

9. What is the hydrogen ion concentration of a 0.01 M solution of formic acid. The ionization constant for the acid is 2.1×10^{-4}. (Hint: Solve a quadratic equation.)

10. A mixture of Ca and Zn weighing 1.00 gm was burned in oxygen yielding 1.34 gm of CaO and ZnO. How much of each metal is in the original mixture. (Hint: let x = grams of Ca and $1.00 - x$ = grams of Zn. Grams of CaO + grams of ZnO = 1.34 gm.)

Chapter 6

Equivalent Equations

6.1. *Types of Equations in Algebra*

At this time it may be desirable to enumerate the various types of equations that have been considered. The student will recall that the equation $a \times b = b \times a$ was used to illustrate, in a general way, the commutative law of multiplication (see Chapter 1). The equality holds no matter what values may be assigned to a and b. This is, therefore, an *identical equation* or the equation is said to reflect an identity. The values assigned must be allowable values. That is, $1/x = 2/2x$ is an identity but the values $x = 0$ must be excluded from consideration because division by zero is not permissible. This type of equation is often referred to as a *universal truth* of arithmetic. All the equations used to illustrate the various axioms of algebra are of this type.

In algebra we are also concerned with equations which are true only for certain numbers that may be substituted for the letters. For example, $x - 2 = 0$ shows an equality that holds for only one value of x, namely $x = 2$. This is a *conditional* equation and is a conditional truth of arithmetic. This equation becomes false for some allowable value(s) of the letters.

6.2. *Classification of Equations*

A considerable part of elementary and advanced algebra is concerned with the solving of conditional equations. The same is true about chemical problems. Henceforth, we shall refer to such conditional equations as simply *equations*. Polynomial equations may be classified according to the *degree* to which the different letters occur. The degree of an equation is the highest degree of all the monomials occurring in the equation with respect to the letters in the equation. For example, $2y + x = 3$ is an equation of first degree in the

x term and in the y term. It is, therefore, a first-degree equation. $y^2 + x = 3$ is of the second degree in y and of the first degree in x.

Considering a general equation in x in the form

$$a_0x^n + a_1x^{n-1} + \cdots + a_{n-1}x + a_n = 0 \ (a_0 \neq 0),$$

the following classification emerges:

$$a_0x + a_1 = 0 \qquad \text{1st degree (linear)},$$
$$a_0x^2 + a_1x + a_2 = 0 \qquad \text{2nd degree (quadratic)},$$
$$a_0x^3 + a_1x^2 - a_2x + a_3 = 0 \qquad \text{3rd degree (cubic)},$$

and for $n = 4$

$$a_0x^4 + a_1x^3 + a_2x^2 + a_3x + a_4 = 0 \qquad \text{4th degree (quartic)}.$$

By convention b is substituted for a_1 in the linear equation so that

$$ax + b = 0 \quad (a \neq 0)$$

represents an equation of the first degree in the unknown x. Linear equations may be solved by the permissible operations discussed in Section 6.3.

6.3. *Equivalent Equations*

Two equations are considered to be equivalent if they have the same roots. That is, when the two equations are solved, the values of the letters in one equation are the same as those in the other. For example, $x - 2 = 0$ and $x + 3 = 5$ are equivalent. When either is solved $x = 2$ is obtained. But $(x - 2)(x - 3)$ has two roots, i.e., $x = 2$ and $x = 3$, and therefore is not equivalent to $x - 2 = 0$.

An equivalent equation can be obtained very easily by the following two axioms:

(1) Adding (or subtracting) the same number to (or from) both members of an equation (therefore, left or right side of the equal sign) yields an equivalent equation.

For example, consider the equation

$$x - 2 = 3$$

and add four to each side

$$x - 2 + 4 = 3 + 4$$
$$x + 2 = 7.$$

The equations $x - 2 = 3$ and $x + 2 = 7$ are equivalent.

(2) Multiplying (or dividing) both members of an equation by any number (except zero) yields an equivalent equation.

For example, consider the equation

$$x - 2 = 3$$

and multiply each side by four

$$4(x - 2) = 4(3)$$
$$4x - 8 = 12.$$

The equations $x - 2 = 3$ and $4x - 8 = 12$ are equivalent.

The above axioms are not used merely to obtain equivalent equations, but are very important in solving algebraic equations. For example, let us solve the equation

$$3x + 8 = -4x + 9.$$

Step 1. Add $4x$ to both sides (Axiom 1)

$$3x + 8 + 4x = 9.$$

Step 2. Simplify

$$7x + 8 = 9.$$

Step 3. Subtract 8 from both sides (Axiom 1)

$$7x + 8 - 8 = 9 - 8.$$

Step 4. Simplify

$$7x = 1.$$

Step 5. Divide each side by 7 (Axiom 2)

$$\frac{7x}{7} = \frac{1}{7}.$$

Step 6. Simplify

$$x = \frac{1}{7}.$$

6.4. *Applications to Chemistry*

1. *Temperature Conversion*

In almost every numerical problem in chemistry equivalent equations are utilized so as to arrive at a solution. Consider, for example, the conversion from one temperature scale to another. To calculate degrees Fahrenheit from degrees Centigrade the following equation is used

$$°F = \tfrac{9}{5}°C + 32.$$

Let us solve for degrees Centigrade in terms of degrees Fahrenheit.

Step 1. Subtract 32 from both sides (Axiom 1)

$$°F - 32 = \tfrac{9}{5}°C + 32 - 32.$$

Step 2. Simplify

$$°F - 32 = \tfrac{9}{5}°C.$$

Step 3. Multiply both sides by $\tfrac{5}{9}$ (Axiom 2)

$$\tfrac{5}{9}(°F - 32) = (\tfrac{9}{5})(\tfrac{5}{9})(°C).$$

Step 4. Simplify

$$\tfrac{5}{9}(°F - 32) = °C.$$

2. *Mole Relationships in Chemical Reactions*

Another type of problem is that dealing with mole relations in chemical reactions. For example, how many moles of oxygen gas are produced from 17 moles of $KClO_3$? It is necessary to have the balanced chemical reaction

$$2\ KClO_3 \rightarrow 2\ KCl + 3O_2.$$

It is seen that 2 moles of $KClO_3$ can produce, by decomposition, 3 moles of O_2. These values can be written into the equation as follows:

$$
\begin{array}{ccc}
2\ \text{moles} & & 3\ \text{moles} \\
2\ KClO_3 \rightarrow & 2\ KCl + & 3\ O_2 \\
17\ \text{moles} & & x\ \text{moles.}
\end{array}
$$

The two ratios are equal to each other

$$\frac{2}{17} = \frac{3}{x}.$$

Multiply both sides by 17

$$2 = \frac{3(17)}{x}.$$

Multiply both sides by x

$$2x = 3(17).$$

Divide both sides by 2

$$x = \frac{3(17)}{2} = 25.5 \text{ moles of } O_2.$$

3. *Weight and Volume Relationships in Chemical Reactions*

The same procedure can be used with weight and for volume relations in chemical reactions. The exercises in Section 6.6 will illustrate the various possibilities.

4. *Titrations*

The titration of a solid base with an acid solution can illustrate the importance of equivalent equations. The number of equivalents of base and acid at the end of the titration must be equal.

$$\text{no. equiv. of acid} = \text{no. equiv. of base.}$$

$$V_A N_A = \frac{gm_B}{gm \text{ mol } wt_B/\text{total positive or negative valence}}.$$

In order to simplify, let $x = $ total positive or negative valence, so that

$$V_A N_A = \frac{gm_B}{gm \text{ mol } wt_B/x}.$$

Now let us solve for x. Using the Fundamental Principle, Chapter 2, multiply the numerator and denominator of the right side by $x/gm \text{ mol } wt_B$

$$V_A N_A = \frac{gm_B \left(\dfrac{x}{gm \text{ mol } wt_B} \right)}{\left(\dfrac{gm \text{ mol } wt_B}{x} \right) \left(\dfrac{x}{gm \text{ mol } wt_B} \right)}$$

$$V_A N_A = gm_B \left(\frac{x}{gm \text{ mol } wt_B} \right).$$

Multiply both sides by gm mol wt_B

$$V_A N_A (gm \text{ mol } wt_B) = (gm_B)(x).$$

Finally, divide both sides by gm_B

$$\frac{V_A N_A (gm \text{ mol } wt_B)}{gm_B} = x = \text{total positive or negative valence.}$$

5. *Equilibrium Constant*

Equivalent equations may be illustrated with problems involving the equilibrium constant or any of the special cases, e.g., ionization, hydrolysis, dissociation of complex ions, and solubility product. In the gaseous equilibrium,

$$2\,SO_2 + O_2 \rightleftharpoons 2\,SO_3,$$

the equilibrium constant is given by

$$K_{eq} = \frac{[SO_3]^2}{[SO_2]^2[O_2]}.$$

Let us solve the equation for $[O_2]$.

Step 1. Multiply both sides by $[O_2]$ to get an equivalent equation

$$K_{eq}\,[O_2] = \frac{[SO_3]^2}{[SO_2]^2}.$$

Step 2. Divide both sides by K_{eq} to get another equivalent equation and the desired one

$$[O_2] = \frac{[SO_3]^2}{K_{eq}\,[SO_2]^2}.$$

Of course, if K_{eq}, $[SO_3]$, and $[SO_2]$ are known, then $[O_2]$ can be calculated.

6.5. *Algebra Problems*

Verify the following identities:

1. $y^2 - 3(y - 4) = y(y - 3) + 12$

2. $\dfrac{3}{x} + \dfrac{1}{x} = \dfrac{4}{x}$

3. $(x + 2)(x + 4) = x^2 + 6x + 8$

4. $\dfrac{1}{z - 2} + \dfrac{1}{z - 3} = \dfrac{2z - 5}{z^2 - 5z + 6}$

5. $\frac{1}{2}v_0 t + \frac{1}{2}v_0 t + \frac{1}{2}at^2 = v_0 t + \frac{1}{2}at^2$

6. $\frac{1}{2}mv^2 = \dfrac{v^2 m}{2}$ (Kinetic energy of a moving body equals $\frac{1}{2}mv^2$.)

Decide whether each of the following is an identity or a conditional equation:

7. $8 - 4x = 5$
8. $(x^3)^2 = x$

9. $\dfrac{7y}{5} - \dfrac{2y}{5} = y$

10. $\dfrac{1}{z} + \dfrac{2}{2z} = \dfrac{3}{3z}$

11. $-5x + 1 = -6$

12. $x^7/x^4 = x^2$

Solve the given equation by using the two axioms to obtain equivalent equations.

13. $8x + 3 = 16$

14. $5x + 7 = 24$

15. $9x - 14 = 17$

16. $-4x + 8 = 9$

17. $-5x - 9 = 10$

18. $-5x - 2 = -8$

19. $-5x + 2 = -7$

20. $4x - 6 = 2$

Solve the following for the indicated letter using the two axioms to obtain equivalent equations.

21. $F = W + \dfrac{Wa}{g}$ for W

22. $A = \dfrac{2R}{R - r}$ for R

23. $\dfrac{1}{C} = \dfrac{1}{C_1} + \dfrac{1}{C_2}$ for C

24. $f = \dfrac{Gm_1m_2}{r^2}$ for m_1

25. $v = \frac{1}{3}\pi r^2 h$ for r

26. $P = 2L + 2w$ for w

27. $C - \dfrac{P - p}{pt}$ for t

28. $V = \dfrac{q}{t_0}\left(\dfrac{1}{r_1} - \dfrac{1}{r_2}\right)$ for r_2

29. $I = \dfrac{E}{r + \dfrac{R}{n}}$ for n

30. $E = \dfrac{T_1 - T_2}{T_1}$ for T_2

6.6. Chemistry Problems

Solve the following for the indicated letter using the two axioms to obtain equivalent equations.

1. $D = \dfrac{M}{V}$ for V

2. $°C = °K - 273$ for $°K$

3. gm atoms of Ca $= \dfrac{\text{gm of Ca}}{\text{at. wt. of Ca}}$ for gm of Ca

4. moles of $SO_2 = \dfrac{\text{gm of } SO_2}{\text{mol wt. of } SO_2}$ for mol wt. of SO_2

5. $\dfrac{V_1}{V_2} = \dfrac{P_2}{P_1}$ for P_1

6. $Pv = nRT$ for V

7. $\dfrac{P_1V_1}{T_1} = \dfrac{P_2V_2}{T_2}$ for V_2

8. $\dfrac{P_1V_1}{T_1} = \dfrac{P_2V_2}{T_2}$ for T_2

9. $PV = \dfrac{g}{M}RT$ for M

10. $\dfrac{r_{H_2}}{r_{CO_2}} = \sqrt{\dfrac{M_{CO_2}}{M_{H_2}}}$ for M_{H_2}

11. $N_AV_A = N_BV_B$ for N_B

12. Lowering of freezing point $= K_f(m)$ for m

13. $K_c = \dfrac{[C]^2}{[A][B]^3}$ for $[C]$

14. $K_p = \dfrac{(P_{CO})^2}{P_{CO_2}}$ for P_{CO}

15. $K_i = \dfrac{[NH_4^+][OH^-]}{[NH_3]}$ for $[OH^-]$

16. $K_d = \dfrac{[Cd^{++}][CN^-]^4}{[Cd(CN)_4^-]}$ for $[CN^-]$

17. $\dfrac{[CN^-]}{[HCN]} = \dfrac{K_i}{[H^+]}$ for $[HCN]$

18. $[Pb^{++}][IO_3^-]^2 = K_{sp}$ for $[IO_3^-]$

19. $Heat = (mass)(sp.ht.)(t)$ for sp.ht.

Chapter 7

Rectangular Coordinates

7.1. Introduction

The solution of an algebraic problem can be presented graphically; the same is true for certain chemical problems. We therefore introduce here what may be called the *rectangular coordinate system.*

The rectangular coordinate system is set up by drawing two perpendicular lines and designating the vertical line as y and the horizontal line as x as shown in Figure 7.1. The point at which the lines meet is called the *origin*. Further,

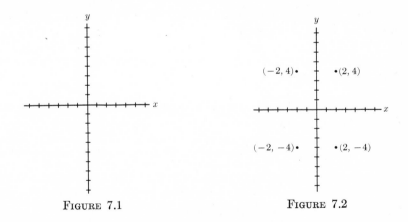

FIGURE 7.1   FIGURE 7.2

the x-axis is called the *abscissa* and the y-axis the *ordinate*. A particular point on the graph is designated by (x, y) so that the point $(2, 4)$ means that $x = 2$, which is two units to the right of the y-axis and $y = 4$, which is 4 units above the x-axis. This is shown in Figure 7.2 along with points $(-2, 4)$, $(-2, -4)$, and $(2, -4)$.

7.2. *The Graph of a Linear Equation*

When a point is located on the coordinate system, it is said to be plotted. By plotting a series of points of an algebraic equation a picture of the equation is obtained. Consider the equation $x + y = 3$. The various (x, y) points are easily obtained by assigning values to x, substituting into the equation, and

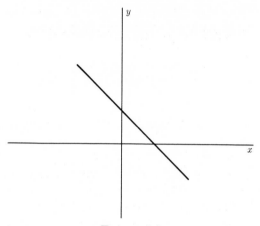

FIGURE 7.3

solving for y values. If this is done, the points $(0, 3)$, $(1, 2)$, $(2, 1)$, $(3, 0)$, $(-1, 4)$, and $(-2, 5)$ are obtained. Locating these on a graph, a straight line is obtained as shown in Figure 7.3.

7.3. *The Slope of a Line*

Any two points in Figure 3 may be used to calculate the slope m of the line because it is given by

$$m = \frac{y_2 - y_1}{x_2 - x_1}$$

where (x_1, y_1) is one point and (x_2, y_2) another point. For example, the points $(0, 3)$ and $(-1, 4)$ may be substituted into the equation to give

$$m = \frac{4 - 3}{-1 - 0} = \frac{1}{-1} = -1.$$

Charles' Law is a generalized statement about a common observation: the volume of a gas is altered with a change in the temperature of the gas at some specified pressure. It is, indeed, the function of laws to explain phenomena in general terms. More specifically, as the temperature of a gas increases its volume increases. We may express this statement in mathematical language as

$$V \propto T,$$

where the sign $\propto$ indicates "varies directly with" or "varies directly as."

When the volume varies directly with the temperature, we say that the volume varies directly with, or is directly proportional to, the temperature. In the form of a proportion this would be

$$\frac{V_1}{V_2} = \frac{T_1}{T_2} \quad \text{or} \quad \frac{V_1}{T_1} = \frac{V_2}{T_2}.$$

Since this is a direct or constant ratio of volume to temperature, we can also say, mathematically,

$$V/T = k \quad \text{or} \quad V = kT$$

where k is the constant. This k is called the *proportionality constant.*

The slope is, roughly, the measure of the slant of a line. The more nearly vertical the line, the larger its slope. A horizontal line will have zero slope; a line making an angle of 45° with the x-axis will have a slope of one. The slope is very useful as we shall see in the next section.

7.4. *Application to Chemistry*

1. *Charles' Law*

The letters V and T may be substituted with other letters which are perhaps more familiar such as

$$y = kx. \tag{1}$$

A plot of y (volume) versus x (temperature) yields a straight line this time passing through the origin. This will occur with gases such as hydrogen, carbon dioxide, nitrogen, etc.

Consider now a typical linear equation such as $x + y = 5$. If small, positive or negative integers are substituted for x, values of y may be obtained. These values of x and y may be plotted on rectangular coordinates illustrating the linear relationship, and the slope of the line may be calculated. (The student should convince himself of this by making the graph.)

The general linear equation, as used in chemistry, is often written as a modification of the first-degree equation in Section 6.2.

$$y = mx + b \quad (m = \text{slope}, b = y \text{ intercept}). \tag{2}$$

The above specific algebraic equation is related to this by writing it as

$$y = -x + 5.$$

In the general equation m is the slope of line. Equation (1) is related to (2) by writing it as

$$y = kx + 0.$$

2. *Specific Heat versus Temperature*

Let us consider a practical laboratory problem from chemistry which will make it clear why the linear equation is important and how the slope of a line is used. In the laboratory it is necessary to measure the specific heat of a liquid at various temperatures and from the data evaluate the constants m and b in the linear equation. This gives an equation which is called an *empirical equation* since it is derived from experimental data. The data from the experiment is as follows:

TABLE I.*

$t°C$	Specific Heat (S)
5.70	0.4000
7.10	0.4009
9.24	0.4040
11.38	0.4061
13.41	0.4091
15.36	0.4103
17.89	0.4133
19.21	0.4151
22.00	0.4178
24.17	0.4208

* From Robert Livingston, *Physico-Chemical Experiments*, Macmillan, New York, 1948, pp. 46–47.

If the above data are graphed, a straight line is obtained. (The student should plot the data.) Two points are chosen from the graph so that the slope (m) can be evaluated. A point P_1 has the coordinates

$$y_1 = 0.4000, \qquad x_1 = 5.70$$

and a point P_2 has the coordinates

$$y_2 = 0.4200, \qquad x_2 = 23.75$$

and the slope is calculated as follows:

$$m = \frac{y_2 - y_1}{x_2 - x_1} = \frac{0.4200 - 0.400}{23.75 - 5.70} = 0.001108.$$

Equation (2) is solved for b so that

$$b = y - mx$$

and using the coordinates for P_2 and the value of m

$$b = 0.4200 - 0.001108 \, (23.75)$$
$$b = 0.3937.$$

The linear equation is now

$$y = 0.001108x + 0.3937$$

or

$$S = 0.001108t + 0.3937$$

since $y =$ specific heat and $x =$ temperature.

The final expression is an empirical equation evaluated graphically and by using the slope of the line. The specific heat of the liquid can now be determined at any temperature merely by substituting a specific value for the temperature.

3. *Vapor Pressure of Liquids*

The pressure exerted by vapor which is in equilibrium with the liquid is known as the *vapor pressure*. The equilibrium between a liquid and its vapor is dependent on the temperature. An equation that shows this relationship quantitatively is

$$\log p = \frac{a}{T} + b$$

where p is the vapor pressure, a and b are constants, and T is the temperature in °K. It should be observed that a straight line is obtained when $\log p$ is plotted against $1/T$; a is the slope and b is the y intercept.

41

4. *Kinetics*

Straight line plots are also encountered in chemical kinetics which is concerned with the rate of reactions and a description of the course of reactions. Problems 1, 4, and 5 in Section 15.6 are illustrative.

7.5. *Algebra Problems*

Plot the graph of each of the following equations:

1. $2x - 6 = y$ 2. $6 - 3x = y$ 3. $x + y = 6$
4. $x + y = -3$ 5. $x + 2y = 0$ 6. $4x - 5 = 3y$
7. $2y = 5$ 8. $2x = -3$ 9. $11x + 5y = 4$
10. $x = 2y$ 11. $3x + 2y = 1$ 12. $x = y$

Find the slope (if it exists) of the line joining the two points for the coordinates given in the following:

13. $(0, 0)$ and $(-3, -4)$ 14. $(-1, 2)$ and $(2, -1)$
15. $(1, 2)$ and $(3, 8)$ 16. $(1, 2)$ and $(4, 11)$
17. $(-1, -2)$ and $(1, 1)$ 18. $(1, 1)$ and $(3, 4)$

Find the slope of the following linear equations and plot the graph of each.

19. $\frac{1}{2}x + 3 = y$ 20. $5 - 2x = y$
21. $1/3x - 2 = y$ 22. $\frac{1}{2} - \frac{1}{4}x = y$
23. $y = x + 4$ 24. $y + 2 = x + 4$
25. $y = 3(x - 5)$ 26. $2x - 3y = 0$

7.6. *Chemistry Problems*

1. Charles' Law states that at constant pressure, the volume of a definite weight of gas is directly proportional to its absolute temperature (°C + 273). The following data were derived experimentally:

Volume (y)	0.5	1.0	2.0
Absolute temp. (x)	136.5	273	546

Plot the curve, calculate the slope, and derive the empirical equation for the data.

2. Do the same as in 1 with the following data:

Volume (liters)	5	10	15	20	25
°K	100	200	300	400	500

3. Gay-Lussac's Law states that the pressure exerted by a gas in a constant volume is directly proportional to the absolute temperature. Do the same as in 1 with the following data:

Pressure (y) mm of Hg	1200	1500	1900
Absolute temp. (x)	298	373	473

4. Using the data in 1, plot volume versus temperature using the ideal gas equation, $PV = nRT$. The pressure is constant and assume one mole of gas ($n = 1$).

5. Using the data in 3, plot pressure versus temperature using the ideal gas equation. Assume one mole of gas.

6. The relation between temperature in degrees Fahrenheit, °F, and degrees Centigrade, °C, is given by

$$°F = \tfrac{9}{5}°C + 32.$$

Construct the graph of this relation.

7. If a gas is heated, it expands in volume according to the equation

$$V = V_0(1 + \tfrac{1}{273}t).$$

If $V_0 = 200$, plot V versus V_0 for $t = 0$ and $t = 273$. (t is the temperature in degrees Centigrade.)

8. Frequency, ν, of radiation belonging to any particular x-ray series (K or L) was found to be quantitatively related to the atomic number, Z, of an element by the expression

$$\sqrt{\nu} = a(Z - \sigma),$$

where a is a proportionality constant and for the K series σ is 1.0. Plot $\sqrt{\nu}$ versus Z for the data:

$\sqrt{\nu} \times 10^{-8}$	Z
10.4	22
10.9	23
11.5	24
11.9	25
12.3	26
12.9	27
13.3	28
13.9	29

(Recall that frequencies have units cm^{-1} since $\nu = c/\lambda$ where $c =$ velocity of light and $\lambda =$ wavelength.)

9. Boyle's Law can be written as $V = k/P$. If the log of both sides is taken $\log V = \log k - \log P$. For one mole of gas at 0°C we obtain $\log V = \log 22.4 - \log P$. Plot $\log V$ against $\log P$ from the following data:

V(liters)	22.4	4.48	2.24	0.002	0.224
P(atm)	1	5	10	20	100

(If necessary, the student should review logarithms in Chapter 13.) The student should be aware that deviations from Boyle's Law occur at high pressures.

10. Arrhenius showed that the rate of a reaction and temperature are related by

$$K = Ae^{-E/RT}$$

where $e = 2.718$ (see Chapter 14) and A and E are quantities characteristic of the reaction in question. Here A is called the frequency factor and represents the number of collisions taking place between molecules, and $e^{-E/RT}$ gives the fraction of collisions possessing activation energy E. The above equation can be written as:

$$\log_{10} k = \log_{10} A - \frac{E}{2.3RT}.$$

Plot the straight line from the data:

log K	-2.90	-2.29	-1.49
$1/T \times 10^3$	1.91	1.75	1.61

What is the slope of the line in the log equation?

11. The following data was obtained experimentally:

Vapor pressure (mm)	13.65	73.88	479.7
$t°C$	70	110	170

Draw the best straight line. Determine the equation for this straight line (that is, obtain numerical values for a and b) and calculate the vapor pressure at 10°C.

Chapter 8

Systems of Equations

8.1. *Pair of Linear Equations*

If there is a system of n equations, it is possible to eliminate one equation so that the number of unknowns is decreased by one. This process is called *elimination* and can be accomplished by substitution, addition, subtraction, or by the method of determinants.

1. *Substitution Method*

Consider the following pair of equations

$$x + 2y = 1 \qquad (1)$$
$$2x + 5y = 3. \qquad (2)$$

These equations may be solved by the method of substitution. (By solving we mean to obtain a value of x and y which will satisfy both equations.) Solve equation (1) for x and then substitute its value into equation (2)

$$x = 1 - 2y$$
$$2(1 - 2y) + 5y = 3.$$

Solving for y gives

$$2 - 4y + 5y = 3$$
$$y = 1.$$

The value of x is obtained by substituting the one for y in equation (1) above,

$$x + 2(1) = 1$$
$$x = -1.$$

2. *Elimination Method*

Equations (1) and (2) may also be solved by the method of *elimination by addition or subtraction*. Equation (1) is multiplied through by -2 to give

$$-2x - 4y = -2$$

and now (2) is added to it

$$
\begin{aligned}
-2x - 4y &= -2 \\
2x + 5y &= 3 \\
\hline
y &= 1.
\end{aligned}
$$

Substituting this value of y into (1) gives $x = -1$. There are several alternate procedures that could have been used besides the one shown above. Equation (1) could have been multiplied through by a positive 2 and then had (2) subtracted from it; (1) could have been multiplied through by 5 and (2) by 2 and y eliminated by subtraction. The student should try the various possibilities.

3. *Method of Determinants*

Equations (1) and (2) may also be solved by the method of *determinants*. This is introduced here not for the purpose of merely having another method, but rather, so that the student will become familiar with the method by solving the simple pair of equations. Determinants find more fruitful use in solving three or more equations. Solving for x by determinants we have

$$x = \frac{\begin{vmatrix} 1 & 2 \\ 3 & 5 \end{vmatrix}}{\begin{vmatrix} 1 & 2 \\ 2 & 5 \end{vmatrix}}$$

and for y we have

$$y = \frac{\begin{vmatrix} 1 & 1 \\ 2 & 3 \end{vmatrix}}{\begin{vmatrix} 1 & 2 \\ 2 & 5 \end{vmatrix}}$$

The student will observe that the denominator in each case is the same and the integers are the coefficients of the x's and y's in (1) and (2). The numerator for the x determinant is changed because the first two integers of the denominator determinant are exchanged for the constants 1 and 3. In the y determinant it is the second two integers that are exchanged for the constants. The x is now evaluated by cross multiplying the integers and subtracting one from the other as follows:

$$x = \frac{5 - 6}{5 - 4} = \frac{-1}{1} = -1.$$

For y we have

$$y = \frac{3 - 2}{5 - 4} = \frac{1}{1} = 1.$$

If any of the numbers in the determinants are negative, then these must be considered as such and the rules of negative numbers followed. Therefore, if the determinant were

$$\begin{vmatrix} 2 & -4 \\ 3 & -5 \end{vmatrix},$$

then it is evaluated as follows:

$$-10 - (-12) = -10 + 12 = 2.$$

8.2. *Double-Notation Method*

Mathematics and science are subject to much generalization, and it is important for the student to become familiar with this method. All of the above manipulations with pairs of equations could have been done in a generalized form using the double-notation method.

In this notation each unknown is designated by an x, but the x's are differentiated by a different subscript. Each coefficient is designated by an a, but the a's are also differentiated by a different subscript. The constant is designated by the letter b, again, with different subscripts. For example, the first equation in a pair of equations would be derived as follows:

$$ax_1 + ax_2 = b.$$

Since it is the first equation, we have

$$a_1x_1 + a_1x_2 = b_1$$

and in order to differentiate between the two coefficients

$$a_{11}x_1 + a_{12}x_2 = b_1. \tag{3}$$

The second equation of the pair is

$$a_{22}x_1 + a_{22}x_2 = b_1. \tag{4}$$

47

The only necessary condition is that

$$\begin{vmatrix} a_{11} & a_{12} \\ a_{21} & a_{22} \end{vmatrix} \neq 0.$$

Using (3) and (4) we can solve the equations by the elimination method. Multiplying both sides of (3) by a_{22} we have

$$a_{22}a_{11}x_1 + a_{22}a_{12}x_2 = a_{22}b_2 \tag{5}$$

and both sides of (4) by a_{12},

$$a_{12}a_{21}x_1 + a_{12}a_{22}x_2 = a_{12}b_2. \tag{6}$$

Now subtract (6) from (5) to get

$$a_{22}a_{11}x_1 + a_{12}a_{21}x_1 = a_{22}b_1 - a_{12}b_2$$
$$x_1(a_{22}a_{11} - a_{12}a_{21}) = a_{22}b_1 - a_{12}b_2$$

$$x_1 = \frac{a_{22}b_1 - a_{12}b_2}{a_{22}a_{11} - a_{11}a_{22}}.$$

Now if (3) had been multiplied by a_{21} and (4) by a_{11}, they would yield

$$x_2 = \frac{(a_{21}b_1 - a_{11}b_2)}{(a_{21}a_{12} - a_{11}a_{22})}.$$

The student is left to derive this.

The student should realize that x_1 represents x in the usual linear x, y equation and x_2 represents the y. We have, therefore, solved for x and y in a most general way and our two equations (3) and (4) represent any pair of linear equations.

Let us now use (3) and (4) and solve for x_1 and x_2 by the method of determinants. Therefore,

$$x_1 = \frac{\begin{vmatrix} b_1 & a_{12} \\ b_2 & a_{22} \end{vmatrix}}{\begin{vmatrix} a_{11} & a_{12} \\ a_{21} & a_{22} \end{vmatrix}} = \frac{a_{22}b_1 - a_{12}b_2}{a_{11}a_{22} - a_{12}a_{21}}$$

and

$$x_2 = \frac{\begin{vmatrix} a_{11} & b_1 \\ a_{22} & b_2 \end{vmatrix}}{\begin{vmatrix} a_{11} & a_{12} \\ a_{21} & a_{22} \end{vmatrix}} = \frac{a_{11}b_2 - a_{21}b_1}{a_{11}a_{22} - a_{12}a_{21}}.$$

8.3. *Type of System and its Solution*

Determinants have another value in that they can be used to ascertain how many solutions a pair of equations has and the type of system it is. Consider, for example, the system

$$x + y = 5, \quad 2x - y = 4.$$

The determinant for the denominator is

$$\begin{vmatrix} 1 & 1 \\ 2 & -1 \end{vmatrix} = -1 - 2 = -3 \neq 0.$$

Because its value does not equal zero the equations are said to be *consistent and independent* and that there is only one solution, namely $x = 3$ and $y = 2$.

Now consider the system

$$x + y = 5$$
$$x + y = 10.$$

The determinant for the denominator is

$$\begin{vmatrix} 1 & 1 \\ 1 & 1 \end{vmatrix} = 0$$

and for the numerator

$$\begin{vmatrix} 5 & 1 \\ 10 & 1 \end{vmatrix} = 5 - 10 = -5 \neq 0.$$

Because the first determinant equals zero and the second does not, the equations are said to be *inconsistent* and have no solution.

For a third type consider the system

$$x + y = 5$$
$$2x + 2y = 10.$$

The determinant in the denominator is

$$\begin{vmatrix} 1 & 1 \\ 2 & 2 \end{vmatrix} = 2 - 2 = 0$$

and for the numerator

$$\begin{vmatrix} 5 & 1 \\ 10 & 2 \end{vmatrix} = 10 - 10 = 0.$$

Because the two equal zero the equations are said to be dependent, and there are many solutions. (The student should convince himself that there are many solutions.)

8.4. *Other Types of Systems*

Systems other than a pair of linear equations are possible. It is possible, for example, to have a linear equation and a nonlinear equation each with the same two unknowns. That is,

$$x + y = 5$$

and

$$xy = 15.$$

The above system can be solved by substitution. Since

$$x = \frac{15}{y}$$

$$\frac{15}{y} + y = 5$$

$$15 + y^2 = 5y$$

and a quadratic equation is obtained,

$$y^2 - 5y + 15 = 0,$$

which can be solved by procedures discussed in Chapter X.

8.5. *Applications to Chemistry*

1. *Analysis of a Mixture of Metals*

As an example of a chemical problem including a pair of linear equations let us consider the reaction of an alloy composed of zinc and aluminum treated with an excess of hydrochloric acid. Both metals will evolve hydrogen gas and knowing the original weight of the alloy and the volume of gas evolved, it is possible to calculate the weight of each metal in the sample used. Consider a laboratory experiment in which a 5 gm mixture of zinc and aluminum evolve 5.61 of H_2 at standard conditions of temperature (0°C) and pressure (1 atm.)

$$1 \text{ eq. wt. of Zn} = \frac{65.4}{2} = 32.7 \text{ gm}$$

$$1 \text{ eq. wt. of Al} = \frac{27}{3} = 9 \text{ gm.}$$

Let

$$x = \text{gm of Zn in original mixture}$$

and

$$y = \text{gm of Al in original mixture.}$$

The following two linear equations arise from the known data:

$$x + y = 5$$

and

$$\frac{x}{32.7} + \frac{y}{9} = \frac{5.6}{11.2}.$$

The 11.2 liters* stem from the fact that the molar volume or the gram molecular volume of any gas at standard conditions is 22.4 liters. The 5.6 liters are divided by 11.2 because the right side must be in units of gram equivalents as is the left side of the equation. Simplifying the second equation we have

$$x + y = 5$$
$$0.031x + 0.111y = 0.5.$$

Using the subtraction-elimination method we multiply the first equation by 0.111.

$$
\begin{array}{l}
0.111x + 0.111y = 0.555 \\
\underline{0.031x + 0.111y = 0.5} \\
0.080x \qquad\qquad = 0.055
\end{array}
$$

$$x = \frac{0.055}{0.080} = 0.7 \text{ gm of Zn}$$

$$y = 5 - 0.7 = 4.3 \text{ gm of Al.}$$

2. *Analysis of a Mixture of Soluble Salts*

Another situation where two linear equations may be set up is in the analysis of a mixture of soluble salts. Two substances which have one common constituent, as for example KCl and NaCl, may be weighed together; the amount of the common constituent, i.e., chlorine, is then determined. For example, a mixture of KCl and NaCl weighed 0.2230 gm. The chlorine in the

---

* The equivalent of a metal is that weight which will evolve 11.2 liters of hydrogen gas at STP conditions.

mixture was determined gravimetrically (i.e., precipitated as AgCl) and weighed 0.1285 gm.

Solution:

Let	x = weight of KCl
and	y = weight of NaCl,
then	$x + y = 0.2230.$

The second linear equation is

$$x \frac{Cl}{KCl} + y \frac{Cl}{NaCl} = 0.1285.$$

Substituting the atomic and formula weights we have

$$x \frac{35.46}{74.56} + y \frac{35.46}{58.46} = 0.1285$$

$$0.4756x + 0.6065y = 0.1285.$$

Solving the pair of linear equations by the substitution method we have

$$x = 0.2230 - y$$
$$0.4756(0.2230 - y) + 0.6065y = 0.1285$$
$$0.1061 - 0.4765y + 0.6065y = 0.1285$$
$$0.1061 + 0.1309y = 0.1285$$
$$0.1309y = 0.0224$$

$$y = \frac{0.0224}{0.1309} = 0.1711 \text{ gm of NaCl}$$

$$x = 0.2230 - 0.1711 = 0.0519 \text{ gm of KCl}.$$

3. *Chemistry Mixing Problem*

Mixing problems may also involve a pair of linear equations in their solution. Consider the problem: What quantities of silver 40% and 82% pure must be mixed together to give 10 gm of silver 70% pure?

Solution:

Let	x = gm of 40% pure silver
and	y = gm of 82% pure silver,
then	$0.60x$ = gm of Ag in 40%
	$0.82y$ = gm of Ag in 82%.

The two linear equations are

$$x + y = 10$$
$$0.60x + 0.82y = 10(.70).$$

Solving by the addition-elimination method

$$-0.60x - 0.60y = -10(.60) = -6$$
$$\underline{0.60x + 0.82y = 10(.70) = 7}$$
$$0.22y = 1$$

$$y = \frac{1}{0.22} = 4.6 \text{ gm of } 40\%$$

$$x = 10 - 4.6 = 5.4 \text{ gm of } 82\%.$$

8.6. Algebra Problems

Solve by each of the methods in Section 8.2.

1. $3x + y = 13$
   $2x + 3y = 4$
2. $4x + 3y = 1$
   $x + 2y = 4$
3. $3x - 2y = 1$
   $x - 3y = 7$
4. $5x - 2y = 4$
   $2x + y = 1$
5. $4x + 3y = 5$
   $2x + y = 2$
6. $x - 3y = 2$
   $5x + y = 2$
7. $3x - 2y = 13$
   $2x + 5y = 4$
8. $3x - 2y = 23$
   $2x + 3y - 2 = 0$
9. $\dfrac{x}{2} - \dfrac{y}{3} = \dfrac{7}{6}$

   $4x - 2y + 2 = 0$
10. $\dfrac{x}{6} + \dfrac{y}{3} = \dfrac{1}{2}$

    $\dfrac{x}{4} + \dfrac{y}{3} = 1$
11. $\dfrac{x}{2} + \dfrac{2y}{5} = 11$

    $\dfrac{-2x}{3} + \dfrac{y}{3} + 3 = 0$
12. $\dfrac{-x}{3} + 1 = y$

    $\dfrac{2x}{5} + \dfrac{4}{5} = 3y + 2$

Decide which of the following systems are consistent and independent, inconsistent, or dependent; solve if possible, and check by graphing each pair of equations.

13. $4x - 6y = 5$
    $2x + 3y = 4$
14. $x - 3y = 5$
    $2x - 6y = 10$
15. $6x + 15y = 21$
    $2x + 5y = 7$
16. $x + 2y = 1$
    $2x + 5y = 3$
17. $3x - 4y = -6$
    $5x - y = 7$
18. $4x - 2 = 6y$
    $3y - 2x = -1$
19. $2x = -y$
    $3x + y = -2$
20. $6x - 8 = -4y$
    $2 - 3x = 2y$

Solve the systems of equations:

21. $x - y = 3, xy = 9$
22. $xy = 3, xy^2 = 12$
23. $\dfrac{4 + y}{3} = x, xy = 2$
24. $(8 + x)4 = y, x^2 = 4$

25. $x = 7y - 4$, $z = 3 + x$, $y = 6$ 26. $xy = 3$, $x = \dfrac{4}{z}$, $y + z = 3$

27. $y - x = 4$, $x = \dfrac{7}{z}$, $zy = 8$ 28. $x - y = 4$, $x^2 = \dfrac{16}{z^2}$, $zy = 8$

8.7. Chemistry Problems

In the following the student should approach each problem by first setting up two equations.

Illustration:

Express 22°F in degrees Centigrade and in degrees Kelvin. Let $x =$ °F, $y =$ °C, $z =$ °K. The two equations are:

$$y = \tfrac{5}{9}(x - 32) \quad \text{and} \quad y = \tfrac{5}{9}x - \tfrac{160}{9}, \ z = y + 273.$$

Solution:

$$y = \tfrac{5}{9}(22) - \tfrac{160}{9} = 12.1 - 17.8 = -5.7$$

and
$$z = -5.7 + 273 = 267.3°\text{K}.$$

(The letters x, y, and z were only to indicate the solution of the problem in the algebraic notation. Certainly °F, °C, and °K could have been used directly.)

1. What amounts of silver 70% and 85% pure must be mixed to give 8.5 gm of silver 80% pure?
2. You have large amounts of 95% and 20% alcohol. How many liters of each must be mixed to give 10 l of a 40% by volume mixture?
3. How many liters of two solutions of acids, one 97% and the other 91%, must be mixed to produce 40 l of a 95% by volume acid solution?
4. Two samples of a solid chemical substance, one 5% and the other 8% pure, must be mixed to give 250 gm of the 7% pure. How much of each must be used?
5. If a Fahrenheit reading is 400 times the Centigrade reading, what is the Centigrade reading?
6. How many grams of dry hydrogen gas are contained in 10 l of hydrogen at 27°C and 2 atm?
7. How many grams of hydrogen gas are contained in 8.5 l of hydrogen measured over water at 25°C and 750 mm? Vapor pressure of water at 27°C is 26.7 mm.
8. Express 22°C in degrees Fahrenheit and in degrees Kelvin.
9. Calculate the vapor pressure of a solution at 30°C containing 65.5 gm of sugar, $C_{12}H_{22}O_{11}$, in 1000 gm of water.
10. In an electrolytic cell a current of 6 amps flows for 20 min and deposits 4.88 gm of zinc. Calculate the equivalent weight of the zinc.
11. Calculate what the hydronium ion concentration must be so that the concentration of Zn^{++} will be 1×10^{-4} M after saturating a solution of a zinc salt with hydrogen sulfide.
12. A mixture of NaBr and NaI weighs 1.320 gm. It yields 2.333 gm of AgBr and AgI. How many grams of NaBr and NaI were there in the original mixture? (Hint: Let $x =$ wt. of NaBr and $y =$ wt. of NaI.)

13. Calculate the number of moles of AgCl dissolved by 0.25 ml of 15 M ammonium hydroxide. (Hint: Set up one equation involving the solubility product constant and the other the dissociation constant of the $Ag(NH_3)_2^+$.)

14. A mixture of CO_2 and SO_3 weighs 2.73 gm and contains a total of 3.6×10^{-2} moles. How many moles of CO_2 and SO_3 are there in the mixture? (Hint: Let x = wt. of CO_2 and y = wt. of SO_3.)

15. A mixture of NaCl and NaBr contains three times as much NaCl as NaBr. Precipitation with Ag^+ yields 150 gm of AgCl and AgBr. Calculate the amount of NaCl and NaBr in the mixture. (Hint: Let x = gm of NaBr, $3x$ = gm of NaCl, y = gm of AgCl, and $150 - y$ = gm of AgBr.)

16. How many liters of 0.4 N and 0.1 N HCl must be mixed to give 2.5 l of 0.2 N HCl? (Hint: Let x = l of 0.4 N HCl and y = l of 0.1 N HCl.)

17. A 20 gm mixture of Na_2CO_3 and Na_2SO_4 when treated with an excess of $BaCl_2$ solution yields a precipitate of $BaCO_3$ and $BaCO_4$. The weight of $BaCO_3$ is twice that of $BaSO_4$. Calculate the number of grams of Na_2CO_3 in the mixture. (Hint: Let x = gm of Na_2CO_3, and y = gm of Na_2SO_4.)

Chapter 9

Irrational Numbers

9.1. Introduction

Irrational numbers were invented because the system of rational numbers, i.e., fractions, was insufficient for our needs. For example, it is impossible to describe the hypotenuse of a right isosceles triangle by a rational number.

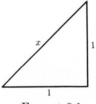

FIGURE 9.1

The hypotenuse of the right triangle is given by $x^2 = (1)^2 + (1)^2 = 2$ and $x = \sqrt{2}$. The square root of two is an irrational number as well as $\sqrt{3}$, $\sqrt{5}$, $\sqrt{6}$, etc. These numbers fill up the gaps that exist on a line. To say that a

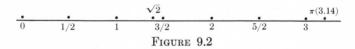

FIGURE 9.2

number is irrational does not mean that it is unreasonable. It means that the number cannot be expressed as a ratio of two integers.

9.2. Reductio Ad Absurdum

We must resort to an indirect proof to show that an irrational number cannot be expressed by a ratio of two integers. A hypothesis is stated and the proof will either support it or contradict it.

Hypothesis: The $\sqrt{2}$ is a fraction so that $\sqrt{2} = a/b$ where $b \neq 0$ and a/b is in its lowest terms. It will now be shown that the assumption that $x^2 = 2$ implies both a and b are even and hence the assumption must be false. For if $x^2 = 2$, then

$$x^2 = \left(\frac{a}{b}\right)^2 = \frac{a^2}{b^2} = 2 \quad \text{and} \quad a^2 = 2b^2.$$

It follows, therefore, that a^2 is even. But this implies that a is even, since if it were odd its square would be odd. Since a is even, this implies

$$a = 2d \qquad (d = \text{integer})$$

and

$$a^2 = (2d)^2 = 4d^2$$
$$4d^2 = 2b^2$$
$$2d^2 = b^2.$$

Therefore, b is also even.

Thus, the assumption that $\sqrt{2} = a/b$ is contradicted and our hypothesis is not true.

9.3. *Square Roots*

The value of $\sqrt{9}$ is 3 and the value of $-\sqrt{9}$ is -3. But the square root of any positive number has two values, i.e., 2 and -2 are square roots of 4 since either one when squared gives 4. The above can be stated as follows:

For any positive number a, $\sqrt{a} = \pm b$ where $(+b)^2 = a$ and $(-b)^2 = a$.

The rules governing the handling of square roots in multiplication and division are

$$\sqrt{ab} = \sqrt{a}\sqrt{b} \quad \text{where} \quad a, b \geq 0$$

and

$$\sqrt{\frac{a}{b}} = \frac{\sqrt{a}}{\sqrt{b}} \quad \text{where} \quad a \geq 0, b > 0.$$

From these rules, then, it follows that

$$\sqrt{45} = \sqrt{9 \times 5} = \sqrt{9}\sqrt{5} = 3\sqrt{5}$$

and

$$\sqrt{\frac{3}{9}} = \frac{\sqrt{3}}{\sqrt{9}} = \frac{\sqrt{3}}{3}.$$

9.4. *Applications to Chemistry*

1. *Diffusion of Gases*

The fact that gases diffuse through the atmosphere is a common-place observation that everyone experiences with the aid of his sense of smell. If camphor is placed in one corner of a room it will be detected, within a short period of time, in every part of the room. It is found that the velocity of a gas is inversely proportional to the square root of its molecular weight. If the velocities of two gases are compared at the same temperature and pressure, they are related as follows:

$$\frac{v_1}{v_2} = \sqrt{\frac{M_2}{M_1}} = \frac{\sqrt{M_2}}{\sqrt{M_1}}$$

where v = velocity and M = molecular weight. To illustrate the use of the equation consider the following problem:

Each molecule of SO_2 has a mass almost exactly double that of an O_2 molecule. If both gases are at the same temperature, which will have molecules with the highest average speed?

Solution:

$$\frac{v_{SO_2}}{v_{O_2}} = \sqrt{\frac{M_{O_2}}{M_{SO_2}}} = \sqrt{\frac{1}{2}} = \frac{\sqrt{1}}{\sqrt{2}} = \frac{1}{\sqrt{2}}$$

or

$$v_{O_2} = \sqrt{2}v_{SO_2}.$$

Obviously the O_2 molecules have the higher speed.

2. *Formation of Precipitate*

When a slightly soluble ionic compound is shaken with water, the ions at the surface of the crystals are dispersed by the action of the solvent, i.e., water. If enough of the ionic solute is present, the rates at which the ions leave and return eventually become equal, and the solution is described as saturated. For any slightly soluble salt the following equilibrium can be written:

$$AB_{(s)} \rightleftharpoons A^+ + B^-.$$

The expression for the solubility product (K_{sp}) expression is

$$[A^+][B^-] = K_{sp}.$$

Knowing the value of the K_{sp}, the concentrations of the ions may be calculated. For example, K_{sp} for $BaSO_4$ is 1×10^{-10} so that

$$[Ba^{++}][SO_4^{--}] = 1 \times 10^{-10}.$$

In the equilibrium

$$BaSO_{4(s)} \rightleftharpoons Ba^{++} + SO_4^{--}$$
$$[Ba^{++}] = [SO_4^{--}] = x$$

and

$$(x)(x) = 1 \times 10^{-10}$$
$$(x)^2 = 1 \times 10^{-10}$$
$$x = \sqrt{1 \times 10^{-10}}$$
$$x = 1 \times 10^{-5} = [Ba^{++}] = [SO_4^{--}].$$

(The more general rules applying to exponential numbers are discussed in Chapter 4.)

3. Chemical Equilibrium

Chemical equilibrium problems involving square roots may be found in Section 5.2, 2.

9.5. Algebra Problems

In the following problems write the given square root as $a\sqrt{b}$ where a is a rational number and b is an integer without perfect square factors.

1. $\sqrt{28}$ 2. $\sqrt{24}$ 3. $\sqrt{96}$ 4. $\sqrt{72}$

5. $\sqrt{\frac{1}{3}}$ 6. $\sqrt{\frac{2}{9}}$ 7. $\sqrt{\frac{8}{28}}$ 8. $\sqrt{\frac{6}{81}}$

9. $\sqrt{\frac{5}{12}}$ 10. $\sqrt{\frac{21}{36}}$ 11. $\sqrt{\frac{1}{5}}$ 12. $\sqrt{\frac{15}{36}}$

In the following problems simplify the square root as above and then simplify the fraction by removing common factors from numerator and denominator.

13. $\dfrac{4 + \sqrt{8}}{4}$ 14. $\dfrac{6 + \sqrt{27}}{6}$ 15. $\dfrac{6 + \sqrt{75}}{6}$

16. $\dfrac{14 + \sqrt{343}}{7}$ 17. $\dfrac{-1 + \sqrt{125}}{3}$ 18. $\dfrac{-4 + \sqrt{24}}{6}$

9.6. Chemistry Problems

1. Each N_2 molecule has a mass very close to fourteen times as great as a H_2 molecule. Which has the higher speed and by how much?
2. The average speed of a H_2 molecule at room temperature and atmospheric pressure

is about 1 mps. What is the average speed of the N_2 molecule under the same conditions?

3. What is the average speed of the O_2 molecule using the information in 2?

4. Calculate the concentration of ions in saturated solutions of AgCl, AgBr, PbSO$_4$, CaCO$_3$, and AgCNS. (See Chapter 4 for discussion of exponential numbers.)

5. Calculate the degree of ionization (α) in a 0.02 M acetic acid solution. (Hint: $\alpha = \sqrt{K/C}$.)

6. What are the [H_3O^+] and [OH^-] in pure water?

7. What is the degree of hydrolysis (h) of the acetate ion in 0.01 M sodium acetate solution. (Hint: $h = \sqrt{K_w/CK_a}$.)

8. Calculate the hydroxide ion concentration in a saturated solution of Mg(OH)$_2$ whose magnesium ion concentration is 0.01 M.

9. Calculate the hydrogen ion concentration in a saturated solution of H_2S if the sulfide ion concentration is 1.4×10^{-16} M. (Use the relation [H^+]^2[S^{--}] = 1.3×10^{-20}.)

10. Determine the NH_3 concentration (moles/liter) in a solution that is 0.005 M in Ag(NH$_3$)$_2$$^+$ and 3×10^{-7} M in Ag$^+$. [Hint: Set up dissociation constant for the Ag(NH$_3$)$_2$$^+$.]

Chapter 10

The Quadratic Equation

10.1. *Introduction*

In Chapter 8 we discussed the linear (first-degree) equation. There are also higher degree equations which can be expressed by the general equation

$$a_0 x^n + a_1 x^{n-1} + \cdots + a_{n-1} x + a_n = 0. \tag{1}$$

Here we shall discuss only the quadratic (second-degree) equation of the type

$$a x^2 + b x + c = 0. \tag{2}$$

There are two solutions to a quadratic equation, and the solutions may be found by substituting the proper values in the quadratic formula

$$x = \frac{-b \pm \sqrt{b^2 - 4ac}}{2a}. \tag{3}$$

The letters a, b, and c correspond to the letters in Equation (2). For example, solve $x^2 - 5x + 6 = 0$ for the two values of x as follows:

$$x = \frac{-(-5) \pm \sqrt{(-5)^2 - 4(1)(6)}}{2(1)}$$

$$x = \frac{5 \pm \sqrt{25 - 24}}{2}$$

$$x = \frac{5 \pm \sqrt{1}}{2} = \frac{5 \pm 1}{2}$$

$$x = 3 \quad \text{or} \quad x = 2.$$

These values may be checked by substituting each into the original quadratic equation, i.e., $x^2 - 5x + 6 = 0$.

For $x = 3$,
$$(3)^2 - 5(3) + 6 = 0$$
$$9 - 15 + 6 = 0$$
$$0 = 0.$$

For $x = 2$,
$$(2)^2 - 5(2) + 6 = 0$$
$$4 - 10 + 6 = 0$$
$$0 = 0.$$

10.2. *Application to Chemistry*

1. *Ionization Constant*

Vinegar is a dilute solution of acetic acid which has the chemical formula CH_3COOH. For the sake of simplicity this formula is shortened to HOAc where Ac stands for the group CH_3CO. In every bottle of vinegar the acetic acid ionizes (i.e., dissociates into its ions) as follows:

$$HOAc \rightleftharpoons H^+ + OAc^-.$$

If the original concentration of HOAc is one molar (1 M) and the amount of H^+ and OAc^- designated as x, then the amount of HOAc remaining in the solution is $1 - x$

$$HOAc \rightleftharpoons H^+ + OAc^-$$
$$1 - x \qquad x \qquad x.$$

The ionization of the HOAc is not complete (indicated by the double arrow) and the $1 - x$ quantity signifies that there remains some unionized HOAc in the solution. The amount of H^+ and OAc^- relative to the amount of HOAc is given by the fraction

$$\frac{[H^+][OAc^-]}{[HOAc]} \quad \text{or} \quad \frac{x \times x}{1 - x}$$

and this fraction is designated by the letter K, the equilibrium constant, so that*

---

*For the derivation of the equilibrium constant relationship the student should consult his chemistry textbook. If x is small as compared to one, the x may be dropped and the solution of a quadratic equation avoided. The rule of thumb for dilute solutions is: use the quadratic formula if the $K < 10^{-2}$; use the simplification if $K > 10^{-2}$.

$$K = \frac{x \times x}{1 - x} = \frac{x^2}{1 - x}. \qquad (4)$$

Since the units moles per liter is understood by the [ ], the unit for K in (4) is determined from

$$K = \frac{\dfrac{\text{moles}}{\text{liter}} \times \dfrac{\text{moles}}{\text{liter}}}{\dfrac{\text{moles}}{\text{liter}}} = \text{moles/liter}.$$

Multiplying both sides of the equation by $1 - x$ we obtain

$$K(1 - x) = x^2$$
$$K - Kx = x^2$$
$$x^2 + Kx - K = 0. \qquad (5)$$

If the value of K (found in Appendix II) were known, then we could substitute it into the derived quadratic equation and obtain values for x. This tells us how much H^+ and OAc^- are in the vinegar.

The K_i is the ionization constant (special case of the equilibrium constant) and used to calculate the acidity of a weak acid solution of the basicity of a weak base solution. For example, to find the hydrogen ion concentration in a 0.25 M HF solution the above quadratic equation can be solved by substituting 7.2×10^{-4} for K_i. Therefore,

$$x^2 + 7.2 \times 10^{-4} \times -7.2 \times 10^{-4} = 0.$$

Substituting into the quadratic formula

$$x = \frac{-7.2 \times 10^{-4} \pm \sqrt{(7.2 \times 10^{-4})^2 - 4(1)(-7.2 \times 10^{-4})}}{2(1)}$$

$$x = \frac{-7.2 \times 10^{-4} \pm \sqrt{51.8 \times 10^{-8} + 28.8 \times 10^{-4}}}{2}$$

$$x = \frac{-7.2 \times 10^{-4} \pm \sqrt{28.8 \times 10^{-4}}}{2}$$

$$x = \frac{-7.2 \times 10^{-4} \pm \sqrt{5.38 \times 10^{-2}}}{2}$$

$$x = 2.65 \times 10^{-2}, \; -5.5 \times 10^{-2}.$$

The second value is discarded because there cannot be a negative value for the concentration of the hydrogen ion. The hydrogen ion concentration is therefore 2.7×10^{-2} M considering two significant digits.

2. *Hydrolysis Constant*

Equation (5) can also be used to determine the hydroxide ion concentration in the hydrolysis of a salt such as sodium cyanide. The hydrolysis of the CN^- ion occurs as follows*:

$$CN^- + H_2O \rightleftharpoons HCN + OH^-.$$

If the original salt solution was 1 M, then

$$CN^- + H_2O \rightleftharpoons HCN + OH^-$$
$$1 - x \qquad\qquad x \qquad x$$

and the K value in equation (4) would be the hydrolysis constant (special case of the equilibrium constant) for the cyanide ion. The value for the hydrolysis constant of an anion base is obtained by dividing the ion product of water (K_w) by the ionization constant of the conjugate acid of the anion. That is,

$$K_h = \frac{K_w}{K_i \text{ (conjugate acid)}}.$$

The value of K_h for the cyanide ion is

$$K_h = \frac{1 \times 10^{-14}}{4.0 \times 10^{-10}} = .25 \times 10^{-4} = 2.5 \times 10^{-5}.$$

Substituting into equation (5)

$$x^2 + 2.5 \times 10^{-5}x - 2.5 \times 10^{-5} = 0$$

and solving for x:

$$x = \frac{-2.5 \times 10^{-5} \pm \sqrt{(+2.5 \times 10^{-5})^2 - 4(1)(-2.5 \times 10^{-5})}}{2(1)}$$

$$x = \frac{-2.5 \times 10^{-5} \pm \sqrt{7.68 \times 10^{-10} + 10.0 \times 10^{-5}}}{2}$$

$$x = \frac{-2.5 \times 10^{-5} \pm \sqrt{10.0 \times 10^{-5}}}{2}.$$

Neglecting the 7.68×10^{-10} since it does not affect the 10.0×10^{-5} appreciably, we have

* The sodium ion does not hydrolyze. The student should refer to a chemistry textbook.

$$x = \frac{2.5 \times 10^{-5} \pm \sqrt{10 \times 10^{-3}}}{2}$$

$$= 5.0 \times 10^{-3} \quad \text{or} \quad -1.0 \times 10^{-2}.$$

The second value is discarded since it is negative.

The concentration of the hydroxide ion is 5.0×10^{-3} M. The simplification referred to in the previous footnote may also be used in problems of hydrolysis. That is, when the value of x is small, so that it does not appreciably affect $1 - x$, it may be neglected. It is then no longer necessary to solve a quadratic equation.

3. *Equilibrium Constant (in Solution)*

General chemical equilibrium problems could also involve quadratic equations. The equilibrium constant value for the equilibrium

$$C_2H_5OH_{(1)} + CH_3COOH_{(1)} \rightleftharpoons CH_3COOC_2H_{5(1)} + H_2O_{(1)}$$
$$\text{alcohol} \qquad \text{acid} \qquad \text{ester} \qquad \text{water}$$

is 4. The problem is to calculate the number of moles of ester which are formed at equilibrium when 2 moles of alcohol are mixed with 1 mole of acid. Let $x = $ moles of ester at equilibrium. Then,

	C_2H_5OH	$+\ CH_3COOH$	$\rightleftharpoons CH_3COOC_2H_5$	$+\ H_2O$
moles at start	2	1	0	0
moles at equilibrium	$2 - x$	$1 - x$	x	x

and the equilibrium constant is given by*

$$K = \frac{(x/v)(x/v)}{\dfrac{2-x}{v}\dfrac{1-x}{v}} = \frac{x^2}{(2-x)(1-x)}$$

$$4 = \frac{x^2}{(2-x)(1-x)}$$
$$4(2-x)(1-x) = x^2$$
$$4(2 - 3x + x^2) = x^2$$
$$8 - 12x + 4x^2 = x^2.$$

Rearranging we have

$$3x^2 - 12x + 8 = 0,$$

---

* In parts (a) and (b) the volume was assumed to be one liter and, therefore, does not affect the result. The volume is included here because it may be something other than one liter. Of course, in the case chosen, the volumes cancel.

a quadratic equation which is solved by using the quadratic formula as described above

$$x = \frac{-b \pm \sqrt{b^2 - 4ac}}{2a} = \frac{12 \pm \sqrt{(12)^2 - 4(3)(8)}}{2(3)}$$

$$x = \frac{12 \pm \sqrt{144 - 96}}{6} = \frac{12 \pm 6.9}{6} = 3.15 \quad \text{or} \quad 8.5 \text{ moles.}$$

There are, of course, two roots to the quadratic equation. One of these roots is physically acceptable. It should be observed that since we started with one mole of acid it is impossible to produce more than one mole of ester. The answer to the above problem is, therefore, 0.85 moles.

Both roots can be checked by substituting the values into the quadratic equation. Therefore,

$$3x^2 - 12x + 8 = 0$$
$$3(.85)^2 - 12(.85) + 8 = 0$$
$$2.16 - 10.20 + 8 = 0$$
$$0 = 0.$$

The same can be done with the value 3.15. The 0.85 is the correct root because it is the physically acceptable one.

4. Equilibrium Constant (Gaseous State)

Another type of problem using a quadratic equation involves the equilibrium

$$N_2O_4 \rightleftharpoons 2\,NO_2$$

whose K_p (this K is calculated from the pressures of the gases) is 0.17 at 27°C. If it is assumed that there is 1 mole of N_2O_4 before any dissociation occurs, then at equilibrium:

$$N_2O_4 \rightleftharpoons 2\,NO_2$$
$$1 - \alpha \quad 2\alpha$$

where α is the degree of dissociation and the total moles are $1 + \alpha$.

$$\text{Total moles} = 1 - \alpha + 2\alpha = 1 + \alpha$$

$$K_p = \frac{(p_{NO_2})^2}{p_{N_2O_4}} = \frac{\left(\dfrac{2\alpha}{1 + \alpha}\right)^2 P^2}{\dfrac{1 - \alpha}{1 + \alpha} P}.$$

(Note that $1 + \alpha$ is a denominator in each case because the p's are partial pressures and P is the total pressure.)

$$K_p = \frac{4\alpha^2\ P}{(1 + \alpha)(1 - \alpha)}.$$

Now consider the following specific problem: What is the extent of dissociation in a 0.5 mole sample of N_2O_4 contained in a 50 liter vessel at 27°C? The number of moles of N_2O_4 and NO_2 at equilibrium are 0.5 $(1 - \alpha)$ and $2(0.5\alpha)$, respectively, and the total number of moles are 0.5 $(1 + \alpha)$.

P is calculated from the ideal gas equation*

$$PV = nRT$$
$$P = nRT/V$$
$$P = \frac{0.5\ (1 + \alpha) \times 0.082 \times 300}{50}$$
$$P = 0.24\ (1 + \alpha) \text{ atm.}$$

Substituting this value into the K_p relationship† we have

$$K_p = \frac{4\alpha^2 \times 0.24\ (1 + \alpha)}{(1 + \alpha)(1 - \alpha)}.$$

Since

$$K_p = 0.17,$$
$$0.17 = \frac{4^2 \times .24\ (1 + \alpha)}{(1 + \alpha)(1 - \alpha)}$$

and the quadratic equation is derived as follows:

$$0.17\ (1 - \alpha) = 4\alpha^2 \times 0.24$$
$$0.17 - 0.17\alpha = 0.96\alpha^2$$
$$0.96\alpha^2 + 0.17\alpha - 0.17 = 0.$$

Obviously, α can be calculated by substituting into the quadratic formula

$$\alpha = \frac{-b \pm \sqrt{b^2 - 4ac}}{2a}$$
$$\alpha = \frac{-0.17 \pm \sqrt{(0.17)^2 - 4(0.96)(-0.17)}}{2(.96)}$$

---

* The student should consult a chemistry textbook for a discussion of the ideal gas equation.

† The K_p is the equilibrium constant when the concentrations of the gases are given in terms of the partial pressures of the gases.

$$\alpha = \frac{-0.17 \pm \sqrt{(0.029 + 0.65)}}{1.9}$$

$$\alpha = \frac{0.17 \pm \sqrt{0.68}}{1.9}$$

$$\alpha = \frac{-0.17 \pm 0.82}{1.9} = -0.52 \quad \text{or} \quad 0.34.$$

The negative root is discarded and the dissociation is 34%.

10.3. *Algebra Problems*

Solve the following equations by use of the quadratic formula (some may have imaginary roots):

1. $6x^2 + 8x + 3 = 0$

2. $Ax + B = \dfrac{1}{Cx}$

3. $2w^2 - 2\sqrt{5}\,w + 7 = 0$

4. $s + 1 = \dfrac{s}{s-2} - \dfrac{1-s}{2}$

5. $\dfrac{4}{3} - \dfrac{y-3}{2x+2} = \dfrac{3}{x}$

6. $12y^2 - 5ay - 3a^2 = 0$

7. $nz^2 + mnz - m^2 = mz$

8. $\dfrac{x-1}{x+2} - 5 = -\dfrac{x}{x-2}$

9. $2t^2 + t - 2 = 0$

10. $0.2x^2 - r + 1 = 0$

11. $\frac{4}{3}y^2 + \frac{1}{2}y = 5$

12. The length of a rectangular is 5 feet more than the width and the area is 36 sq. ft. What is the perimeter of the rectangular?

13. Find two consecutive numbers whose product is 156.

14. Two numbers differ by 3 and their product is 130. Find the numbers.

10.4. *Chemistry Problems*

(The student should consult his chemistry textbook if he has difficulty with some of these problems.)

1. Find the hydrogen ion concentration of a 0.1 M solution of phosphorous acid. (The second ionization may be neglected.)

2. Determine the concentration of the hydrogen sulfite ion in a 0.05 M solution of sulfurous acid. (Neglect the second ionization.)

3. Calculate the acidity of a 0.02 M solution of arsenic acid. (Neglect the second and third ionizations.)

4. What is the hydrogen ion concentration of a 0.001 M solution of formic acid?

5. Calculate the hydroxide ion concentration of a 0.001 M solution of NaHS. The hydrolysis constant for HS^- is 7.7×10^{-3}.

6. Calculate the hydroxide ion concentration of a 0.05 M solution of Na_2HPO_4. The

hydrolysis constant for HPO_4^{--} is 1×10^{-2}. (Neglect the second step in the hydrolysis.)

7. Determine the basicity of a 0.001 M solution of sodium hydrogen carbonate. The K_h for HCO_3^- is 1.4×10^{-4}. Is it necessary to use the quadratic formula or could the simplification have been used?

8. How many moles of ester are formed at equilibrium when 3 moles of ethyl alcohol are mixed with 1 mole of acetic acid? See example in introduction.

9. When SO_2 and NO_2 are mixed the following equilibrium is established which at some specific temperature has a value of 3,

$$SO_2 + NO_2 \rightleftharpoons SO_3 + NO.$$

The equilibrium mixture contains 0.80 moles of SO_2, 0.10 moles of NO_2, 0.60 moles of SO_3, and 0.40 moles of NO. Calculate the number of moles of each gas if 1 mole of NO is added to the reaction flask. Hint: there will be $(0.8 + x)$ moles of SO_2, $(0.10 + x)$ moles of NO_2, $(0.60 - x)$ moles of SO_3, and $(1.40 - x)$ moles of NO.

10. What is the extent of dissociation in a 69 gm sample of N_2O_4 in a 20 l flask at 27°C? See problem 4 in the Introduction.

11. At 55°C, K_p for the equilibrium in problem 10 is 0.66. Compute the percent dissociation of 1 mole of N_2O_4 at this temperature in a 10 liter flask.

12. If a mole of hydrogen is mixed with b moles of iodine, and $2x$ moles of hydriodic acid are formed, set up the quadratic equation which would allow you to solve for x. (Hint: when equilibrium is established, $a - x$ is the amount of hydrogen, and $b - x$ is the amount of iodine present.)

13. In a 10 liter flask of 0.5 moles of hydrogen and 0.5 moles of iodine are reacted at 448°C. The equilibrium constant value at this temperature is 50. How many moles of iodine remain unreacted when equilibrium is established? Hint: Let x = moles of H_2 and I_2 at equilibrium and $2x$ = moles of HI formed.

Chapter 11

Functions and Graphs

11.1. *Introduction*

Consider traveling in a car from one city to another. The time (t) it takes will depend upon the distance (s) between the two cities and the speed (v) of the car. The time is, therefore, a function of the distance and the speed and in mathematical notation it is represented by

$$t = f(s, v).$$

The notation says that when s or v varies t will also vary. Because these letters represent unspecified elements of a set of numbers they are called *variables*.

The distance a body falls depends upon the time that it is falling. The distance (s) is given by

$$s = \tfrac{1}{2}gt^2$$
$$s = \tfrac{1}{2}(32)t^2$$
$$s = 16t^2.$$

The distance is, therefore, a function of time and we write

$$s = f(t).$$

This equation says that s depends on t and when t varies s also varies or a change in t induces a corresponding change in s. The g (32 ft/sec²) represents a set consisting of one number only and is called a *constant*. The symbols s and t are variables.

Consider the area of a square which is easily found by the product of the lengths of the two sides. If the side (x) increases in length, then the area (A) becomes larger which means that A is dependent on x or

$$A = f(x).$$

This is seen in the following diagram.

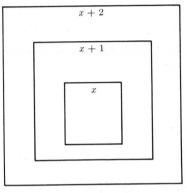

FIGURE 11.1

When x increases to $x + 1$, the area is increased, etc.

11.2. *Functions*

Definition: A function f is a relationship which associates with every permissible value of x, a corresponding value of y. We then say that y is a function of x and write

$$y = f(x).$$

In the functions that we will study the permissible values for x will be real numbers so that the values of y will also be real numbers. (It should be clear to the student that any other two letters could have been chosen.)

A function may be defined or described either by an algebraic expression or by a set of ordered pairs. Consider the function

$$y = f(x) = x + 8$$

where there is a value of y corresponding to every permissible value of x. Therefore, when $x = 4$, $y = 14$, etc. The algebraic expression, $x + 8$, determines a function.

Prior to graphing the equation $y = x + 8$ it is necessary to find values of y corresponding to values of x. This yields the data

x	y or $f(x)$
1	9
2	10
3	11
4	12

which is a collection of ordered pairs constituting a set of ordered pairs, each member of the set (1 and 9, 2 and 10, etc.) being an ordered pair. This set of ordered pairs constitutes the function determined by the equation, $y = x + 8$.

11.3. *Graphing Functions*

Let us consider a linear function and two functions of higher order.

Example 1. Let $y = f(x) = 5 - x$. Then when

$$x = 0 \qquad f(x) = 5$$
$$x = 1 \qquad f(x) = 4$$
$$x = -1 \qquad f(x) = 6$$
$$x = 2 \qquad f(x) = 3.$$

This gives us a set of ordered pairs which also describes the function and allows us to draw the graph in Figure 11.2.

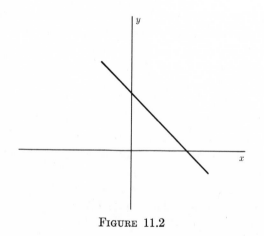

Figure 11.2

Example 2. Let $y = f(x) = x^3$. Then when

$$x = 0 \qquad f(x) = 0$$
$$x = 1 \qquad f(x) = 1$$
$$x = 2 \qquad f(x) = 8$$
$$x = -2 \qquad f(x) = -8$$
$$x = 3 \qquad f(x) = 27$$
$$x = -3 \qquad f(x) = -27, \text{ etc.}$$

This data yields the graph in Figure 11.3.

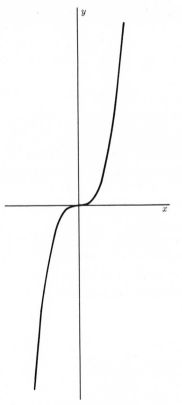

FIGURE 11.3

Example 3. Let $y = f(x) = x^2 - 3x - 5$. Then when

$$x = 0 \qquad f(x) = -5$$
$$x = 1 \qquad f(x) = -7$$
$$x = -1 \qquad f(x) = -1$$
$$x = 2 \qquad f(x) = -7$$
$$x = -2 \qquad f(x) = 5, \text{ etc.}$$

This data yields the parabola in Figure 11.4.

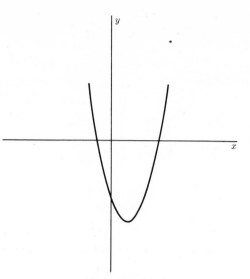

FIGURE 11.4

The roots (i.e., the solutions) for this equation may be found graphically by noting the value of x where the curve crosses the x-axis and with these values $x^2 - 3x - 5$ equals zero.

11.4. *Applications to Chemistry*

In many chemistry problems in beginning chemistry it is important to be able to apply the laws of algebra to specific, well-defined properties. These definitions can often be expressed in algebraic form and manipulated in a similar manner.

1. *Density*

Thus density is defined as the mass of an object divided by its volume. Expressed algebraically:

$$\text{Density} = \text{Mass/Volume}$$

or

$$D = M/V.$$

At a specific temperature the density of a substance is constant and the mass and volume may be variables. If both sides of the equation are multiplied by V, we have

$$DV = \text{M}.$$

It is seen then as the volume varies the mass will vary.

The original equation contained three properties and if we have numbers for any two of the properties it is possible to calculate the numerical value of the third. If a series of M values are given and the V values calculated, these will constitute a set of ordered pairs and they could be shown graphically. (This is not usually done.)

2. *Boyle's Law*

If a given mass of gas (m) is kept in a vessel and its volume (V) changed, there will be a corresponding change in its pressure (P) with the product PV remaining the same. Algebraically,

$$PV = k$$

(m and temperature are kept fixed) where P and V are variables and k is a constant. Ordered pairs such as the following can be obtained in the laboratory and graphed.

P	2.0	1.0	0.5
V	0.5	1.0	2.0

3. *Freezing Point Depression*

When a non-volatile substance is dissolved in a liquid the freezing point of the liquid is lowered, and the algebraic relationship is

$$T_f = K_f m$$

where T_f is the change in the freezing point temperature, K_f is a constant for a particular substance and m is the molality* of the solution. As m varies T_f will also vary; if one is known, the other can be calculated.

11.5. *Algebra Problems*

Write an algebraic expression for $f(x)$ in the following:

1. There is a number which is 6 greater than a given number.
2. There is a number which is the square of a given number.
3. There is a number which is the reciprocal of a given number.
4. There is a number which is the square of the sum of two given numbers.
5. If $f(x) = x^3 - 2x^2 + 5x - 6$, find $f(3)$.
6. If $f(y) = \dfrac{4y + 3}{y + 9}$, find $f(12)$.

* A 1 molal solution contains a mole of solute per kilogram of solvent.

7. If $f(t) = t^2 + 5t - 2$, find $f(2)$.

8. Determine the simplest function knowing the following ordered pairs:

$$x \quad 1 \quad 2 \quad 3$$
$$y \quad 3 \quad 4 \quad 5$$

9. Determine the simplest function knowing the following ordered pairs:

$$x \quad 1 \quad 2 \quad 3$$
$$y \quad -3 \quad -2 \quad -1$$

10. Determine the simplest function knowing the following ordered pairs:

$$x \quad 1 \quad 2 \quad 3$$
$$y \quad 1 \quad 4 \quad 9$$

Graph the given function as smooth curves after first finding at least ten ordered pairs.

11. $f(x) = 2x - 6$
12. $f(x) = \frac{1}{3}x - 1$
13. $f(x) = 2x^2 + 4x - 5$
14. $f(x) = x^2 + 2x - 3$
15. $f(x) = x^2 - 5x + 2$
16. $f(x) = x^2 + x - 100$
17. $f(x) = x^2 - 1$
18. $f(x) = 4x^2 - 9x - 36$
19. $f(x) = x(x - 2) - 1$
20. $f(x) = 4x + 3$
21. The ordered pairs for some function are

$$y \quad 5 \quad 20 \quad 45 \quad 80$$
$$x \quad 1 \quad 2 \quad 3 \quad 4$$

Graph this set of ordered pairs, and note that it does not yield a straight line through the origin. Regraph the function but plot y against corresponding values of x^2; for example, 45 and 9 would be the third point. Is this graph a straight line? Write an equation derived from this graph for the function.

22. A function has the following set of ordered pairs:

$$y \quad 16.0 \quad 4.0 \quad 1.8 \quad 1.0$$
$$x \quad 1 \quad 2 \quad 3 \quad 4$$

A proportionality constant of 16 relates y and x in an equation. Graph the data and determine the function.

23. A function has the following set of ordered pairs:

$$y \quad 3 \quad 10 \quad 17 \quad 24$$
$$x \quad 0 \quad 1 \quad 2 \quad 3$$

These data give a straight line that does not go through the origin. Notice that as each point is dropped three units down the y-axis the line goes through the origin. Plot this graph; that is, plot $(y - 3)$ against values of x. For instance, 14 and 2 would be the third ordered pair. Derive an equation for the data.

11.6. *Chemistry Problems*

In each of the following identify any variables and/or constants in the equations:

1. $°C = \frac{5}{9}(°F - 32)$

2. $K.E. = \frac{1}{2}mv^2$

3. $V/T = k$ (Charles' Law)

4. $PV/T = k$ (Combined Gas Law)

5. $PV = nRT$ (Ideal Gas Equation)

6. $\pi = cRT$ (Osmotic Pressure)

7. $\Delta T_b = K_b m$ (Boiling Point Elevation)

8. $K_{eq} = \dfrac{[HI]^2}{[H_2][I_2]}$ (Temperature is fixed and H_2 is added)

9. $K_{sp} = [Ag^+][Cl^-]$ (Temperature is fixed and NaCl is added)

10. $K_i = \dfrac{[H^+][C_2H_3O_2^-]}{[HC_2H_3O_2]}$ (Temperature is fixed and $NaC_2H_3O_2$ is added)

11. $pH = -\log [H_3O^+]$

12. Specific rate $= k\,[H_2][I_2]$

13. $E_{ox} = E°_{ox} - \dfrac{2.3RT}{nF} \log \dfrac{[Ox]}{[Red]}$

14. $\log \dfrac{k_1}{k_2} = \dfrac{(T_1 - T_2)E_{act.}}{2.3RT_1T_2}$ (Arrhenius' Equation)

15. In each of the above express one (sometimes two) of the letters as a function of the other variables.

Example: $°K = °C + 273$.
Solution: $°K = f(°C)$.

Chapter 12

Inequalities

12.1. Introduction

In Example 3 of Chapter 11 the function $x^2 - 3x - 5$ was discussed. In that example we obtained two values of x that would make the function equal to zero. But there are also values of x which make the function equal to some value other than zero.

There are two basic principles governing inequalities. They are:

(1) If h is a positive number and $a = b + h$, then a is greater than b ($a > b$).
(2) If h is a negative number and if $a = b + h$, then a is smaller than b ($a < b$).

Conversely:

(1) If $a > b$, then there exists a negative number h such that $a = b + h$.
(2) If $a < b$, then there exists a negative number h such that $a = b + h$.

Example 1.

$$9 = 6 + 3 \quad \text{implies that } 9 > 6$$
$$5 = 6 - 1 \quad \text{implies that } 5 < 6.$$

Inequalities may be manipulated in much the same way as equalities. One difference is that the order of the inequality may be changed. An inequality retains the order of its inequality if:

(1) The same number is added to both sides.
(2) The same number is subtracted from both sides.
(3) Both members are multiplied by the same positive number.
(4) Both members are divided by the same positive number.

The order of an inequality is reversed if:

(1) Both members are multiplied by the same negative number.

(2) Both members are divided by the same negative number.

Example 2.

$$8 > 6$$
$$8 + 2 > 6 + 2$$
$$8 - 2 > 6 - 2$$
$$8(3) > 6(3)$$
$$8/4 > 6/4$$
$$8(-3) < 6(-3)$$
$$8/-4 < 6/-4.$$

The above principle may be used to solve linear inequalities of the type

$$ax + b > c.$$

Example 3. For what values of x is $5x - 9 > 0$?

Step 1. Add 9 to both members:

$$5x - 9 + 9 > 0 + 9$$
$$5x > 9.$$

Step 2. Divide both members by 5:

$$5x/5 > 9/5$$
$$x > 9/5.$$

Therefore, $5x - 9 > 0$ if $x > 9/5$.

This means that all values greater than 9/5 will satisfy the inequality but 9/5 itself does not; if 9/5 is substituted for x it will make the left side equal to zero.

12.2. *Quadratic Inequalities*

Quadratic inequalities of the type

$$ax^2 + bx + c > 0$$

can be solved by studying the plot that one obtains. For this type of quadratic a parabola is obtained and the solution of the inequality is reduced to finding what part of the curve lies above the x-axis and what part lies below it. $ax^2 + bx + c > 0$ corresponds to the part of the curve that lies above the x-axis; $ax^2 + bx + c < 0$ corresponds to that part of the curve that lies below the x-axis. Of course, $ax^2 + bx + c = 0$ corresponds to the two values of x where the curve crosses the axis.

Example 4. For what values of x is $x^2 + x - 6 > 0$?

Step 1. Let $y = x^2 + x - 6$ and obtain values for y for specific values of x and plot the curve. (See Figure 12.1.)

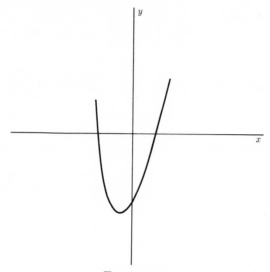

FIGURE 12.1

Step 2. Identify the two values of x where the curve crosses the x-axis

$$x = 2 \quad \text{and} \quad x = -3.$$

Step 3. The values of x that lie above the x-axis will satisfy the inequality. Therefore, x is greater than 2 ($x > 2$) and x is smaller than -3 ($x < -3$). The solution may be written as

$$2 < x < -3.$$

12.3. *Solving Quadratic Inequalities*

Quadratics, of course, were discussed above, but in this section we shall extend the discussion and also introduce an alternate method of solving inequalities.

Example 5. Solve the inequality $x^2 - 5x + 4 \leq 0$ by the graphical method.

Step 1. Let $y = x^2 - 5x + 4$ and plot the curve. (See Figure 12.2.)

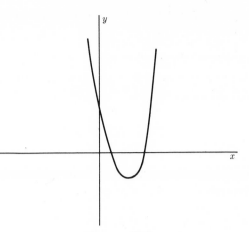

FIGURE 12.2

Step 2. Find the values of x to make the function equal to zero.

$$x = 1 \quad \text{and} \quad x = 4$$

Step 3. Find values of x to make the function less than zero.

$$x > 1 \quad \text{and} \quad x < 4$$

Step 4. Combine the solutions in Steps 2 and 3.

$$1 \leqq x \leqq 4.$$

Example 6. Solve the same inequality by the algebraic method.

Step 1. To solve $x^2 - 5x + 4 \leqq 0$ we factor $x^2 - 5x + 4$ and have

$$(x - 1)(x - 4) \leqq 0.$$

Step 2. The product of the two factors should equal zero so that

$$\text{either} \quad (x - 1) = 0 \quad \text{or} \quad (x - 4) = 0.$$

Step 3. The product should be negative in order to be less than zero so that we either have

$$(x - 1) < 0 \quad \text{and} \quad (x - 4) > 0$$

or

$$(x - 1) > 0 \quad \text{and} \quad (x - 4) < 0.$$

Combining we have

$$(x - 1) \leq 0 \quad \text{or} \quad (x - 4) \geq 0$$

but not both.

Solving for x in each inequality, we obtain

$$x \leq 1 \quad \text{and} \quad x \geq 4$$

or

$$x \geq 1 \quad \text{and} \quad x \leq 4.$$

Step 4. Eliminate the first set because it is impossible to have x less than 1 and, at the same time, greater than 4. The second set is possible and the solution of the inequality may be summed up as

$$1 \leq x \leq 4.$$

12.4. *Applications to Chemistry*

1. *Solubility Product Constant*

(a) Hard water may be softened by chemical treatment. Water for a city is usually treated by the addition of chemicals, followed by sedimentation when the water is allowed to stand in large reservoirs, and then by filtration through beds of sand.

The hardness of water is due mainly to calcium (as the ion, Ca^{++}) and magnesium (as the ion, Mg^{++}); it is these ions that form precipitates (curds) with ordinary soap. In softening water sodium carbonate may be used to precipitate the above ions as calcium carbonate ($CaCO_3$) and magnesium carbonate ($MgCO_3$) respectively.

Whether a precipitate forms depends on the amount of ions in the water. The product of the amounts determines whether a precipitate is formed (i.e., whether a saturated solution is produced). If the product is greater than some specific constant, then a precipitate is formed; if the product is equal to or less than the constant, then a precipitate will not form. For example, the constant for calcium carbonate is 7.5×10^{-9} and if

$$xy > 7.5 \times 10^{-9}$$

where x = amount of calcium ion (Ca^{++})
y = amount of carbonate ion (CO_3^{--}),

a precipitate of $CaCO_3$ will form; but if

$$xy \leq 7.5 \times 10^{-9},$$

then $CaCO_3$ does not precipitate.

The constant for magnesium carbonate is 1×10^{-5} and if

$$zy > 1 \times 10^{-5}$$

where z = amount of magnesium ion (Mg^{++}), a precipitate of magnesium carbonate will form; but if

$$zy \leqq 1 \times 10^{-5},$$

then no precipitate forms.

(b) For the precipitation of a slightly soluble electrolyte it is necessary to bring together in the same solution the ions of that electrolyte, in such amounts that the product of ion concentrations exceeds the solubility product of the compound. Thus, in order to precipitate $Mg(OH)_2$ the concentration conditions are such that:

$$[Mg^{++}][OH^-]^2 > K_{sp} \ (1.2 \times 10^{-11}).$$

Sodium hydroxide or ammonium hydroxide can precipitate Mg^{++} from solution (assuming, of course, a high enough metal ion concentration). An ammonia solution though with an ammonium salt added will not precipitate Mg^{++}. The condition now is

$$[Mg^{++}][OH^-]^2 < 1.2 \times 10^{-11}.$$

The equilibrium in ammonia solution is expressed as

$$\frac{[NH_4^+][OH^-]}{[NH_3]} = K_i = 1.8 \times 10^{-5}.$$

In the presence of a high concentration of ammonium ion:

$$\frac{[NH_4^+][OH^-]}{[NH_3]} > 1.8 \times 10^{-5}.$$

The reaction $NH_4^+ + OH^- \rightarrow NH_3 + H_2O$ is favored until the concentrations of the ions have been lowered, and the concentration of NH_3 increased, so that again:

$$\frac{[NH_4^+][OH^-]}{[NH_3]} = 1.8 \times 10^{-5}.$$

The failure to get a precipitate of $Mg(OH)_2$ is the consequence of too low a concentration of hydroxide ion.

12.5. *Algebra Problems*

Solve the following inequalities:

1. $x - 9 < 0$ 2. $x - 3 < 0$ 3. $x - 4 > 0$
4. $5x + 10 > 0$ 5. $5x - 10 > 0$ 6. $7x + 3 > 15$
7. $4x + 2 < 2x + 7$ 8. $2x - 8 < 0$ 9. $3x - 9 > 0$

10. $\dfrac{8 - x}{2} > 2x - 1$ 11. $\dfrac{2 - x}{3} < \dfrac{4x - 3}{2}$ 12. $(x + 5)(x - 1) < 0$

13. $(x - 2)(x + 4) > 0$ 14. $(x - 2)(x + 3) > 0$ 15. $(x - 1)(x + 2) < 0$.
16. Make a sketch showing points representing the following numbers on a horizontal line directed to the right:

$$3, -1, 0, -1.5, \sqrt{2}, 2, -2, -3.$$

Rewrite the numbers in increasing order, giving the result as a continued inequality of the form $x < y < z$, etc.
17. For two real numbers x and y, what conclusion can you draw if you can show that $x \geq y$ and that $x \leq y$?
18. Indicate whether the following are true or false:

a. $-2 \geq -4$ b. $0 > -2$ c. $\frac{1}{3} > \frac{1}{2}$
d. $-\frac{1}{4} > -\frac{1}{2}$ e. $\frac{3}{2} > \frac{3}{4}$ f. $2 - 2^2 < -3^2$.

Solve the given inequalities by the algebraic method.

19. $x^2 - 7x + 12 > 0$ 20. $x^2 - 6x + 8 > 0$
21. $x^2 - 4x + 3 > 0$ 22. $x^2 - 9x > -20$
23. $x^2 - 18x > -45$ 24. $x^2 > -4x + 12$
25. $x^2 - 6x < -9$ 26. $-x < 2 - 3x^2$
27. $x^2 + 9x < -14$ 28. $x^2 > -6x - 5$.

Solve the given inequalities by the graphical method.

29. $3x - 5 > 0$ 30. $2x + 1 > 0$ 31. $2x - 3 < 6$
32. $x^2 > 12 - x$ 33. $x^2 + 2x < 3$ 34. $2x^2 + x - 6 \geq 0$
35. $x^2 + y^2 > 4$ 36. $x^2 + y^2 \leq 9$ 37. $x^2 - 4y \geq 0$
38. $x^2 - y^2 > 1$.

12.6. *Chemistry Problems*

1. For each of the following slightly soluble substances, indicate in mathematical form the conditions for their precipitation and dissolution (use K_{sp} values in Appendix II): AgI, $Mg(OH)_2$, CaC_2O_4, Ag_2SO_4, MnS, Hg_2I_2, and $PbBr_2$. Sample: $[Ag^+][I^-] > 1 \times 10^{-16}$, $[Ag^+][I^-] < 1 \times 10^{-16}$.
2. In a series of solutions the chloride ion concentration and the silver concentration are as follows.

Table ($K_{sp} = 1.2 \times 10^{-10}$)

Cl^-	Ag^+
6.4×10^{-3}	1.7×10^{-8}
8.0×10^{-3}	0.2×10^{-7}
10.5×10^{-3}	2.07×10^{-8}
30.3×10^{-3}	0.388×10^{-8}

Determine whether a solid AgCl will form.

3. In qualitative analysis the chlorides of silver, mercurous and lead precipitate when a slight excess of dilute HCl is added to a solution containing these ions. Express the conditions in terms of K_{sp} and inequalities.
4. In one qualitative analysis scheme Group II cations are separated from Group III cations by use of H_2S in an acid solution. Concentrations are such that cadmium sulfide will precipitate but zinc sulfide will not. Express the conditions in terms of K_{sp} and inequalities.
5. Will $Mg(OH)_2$ precipitate in a solution where $[Mg^{++}] = 0.6$ M and the $[OH^-] = 1.1 \times 10^{-4}$ M?
6. Will ZnS precipitate in a solution where $[Zn^{++}] = 0.1$ M and $[S^{--}] = 4.5 \times 10^{-24}$?

Chapter 13

Logarithms

13.1. *Introduction*

The *logarithm* of a number is the power to which the base must be raised to equal that number. Thus $100 = 10^2$; the logarithm (log) of 100 is 2. It is written as $\log 100_{10} = 2$, and read, "log of 100 to the base 10 equals 2." In this chapter we shall write $\log 100 = 2$ and assume the base 10. Logarithms to the base 10 are known as *common logarithms*. Logarithms with the base e ($e = 2.7182^+$) are called *natural logarithms*, but these will be considered in Chapter 15.

Considering now common logarithms it is evident from the above definition that since

$$10^0 = 1 \qquad 10^{-1} = 0.1$$
$$10^1 = 10 \qquad 10^{-2} = 0.01$$
$$10^2 = 100 \qquad 10^{-3} = 0.001,$$

it follows that

$$\log 1 = 0 \qquad \log 0.1 = -1$$
$$\log 10 = 1 \qquad \log 0.01 = -2.$$
$$\log 100 = 2 \qquad \log 0.001 = -3.$$

It is observed that as the number increases the logarithm of the number increases.

The log of $567 = 2.7536$ correct to four decimal places. The digit before the decimal point is the characteristic, i.e., 2, and the decimal part is called the mantissa, i.e., 0.7536.

13.2. *Finding the Characteristic of a Logarithm*

The characteristic of a log of a number equal to or greater than one is one less than the number of digits to the left of the decimal point. Therefore, the 567 has three digits to the left of the decimal, and, as said above, its characteristic is two. For the 23 300, it is four, etc.

The characteristic of a number less than one is negative and is one more than the number of zeros directly after the decimal point. For the decimal fraction 0.00264, which has two zeros directly after the decimal point, has a characteristic of $\bar{3}$ or $+7 - 10$. For 0.0234, it is $\bar{2}$ or $+8 - 10$, etc.

It will be observed that the number 567 when written in exponential form is 5.67×10^2 (always with one digit to the left of the decimal point); the characteristic is the exponent, i.e., two. The number 0.00264 is written as 2.64×10^{-3} and its characteristic is $\bar{3}$ or $+7 - 10$.

Example 1. What is the characteristic of the following numbers?

Number	Characteristic
5297	3
3	0
84.3	1
6.474	0
800	2
843	2
70	1

Example 2. What is the characteristic of the logarithm of 0.3485?

$$\bar{1} \quad \text{or} \quad 9 - 10.$$

Example 3. What is the characteristic of the logarithm of 0.0513?

$$\bar{2} \quad \text{or} \quad 8 - 10.$$

13.3. *Finding the Mantissa of a Logarithm*

The mantissa of a logarithm is found by consulting a logarithm table (see Appendix III). In this table, the mantissas of the logarithms of all integers from 1 to 999 are recorded correct to four decimal places. Five-, six-, or seven-place tables are also available but for our purposes a four-place table will be very satisfactory.

In a four-place log table the first two digits of the number are listed in the left column under N and the third in a row across the top of the table from 0 to 9. All the numbers from 0000 to 9996 are mantissas.

The mantissa for a number is located where the row for the first two digits intersects with the column for the third digit. Any mantissa is positive and written as a decimal even though the decimal point is omitted in the table. Thus, 0000 is really .0000.

Example 4. What is the mantissa for each of the following numbers?

Number	Mantissa
845	9269
720	8573
30	4771
5.0	6990
0.92	9638

13.4. *Finding the Logarithm of a Number*

Let us consider again the number 567 and determine its logarithm from the table. We know the characteristic is two because there are three digits to the left of the decimal point or because it can be expressed as 5.67×10^2.

$$\log 567 + 2.\text{_____}.$$

On the table find 56 under N and then proceed along the top row until seven is reached. Come down until the column and the row intersect and

$$\log 567 = 2.7536.$$

Example 5. Find the log of 72.8.

$$\log 72.8 = 1.\text{_____}$$
$$\log 72.8 = 1.8621.$$

Example 6. Find the log of 0.464.

$$\log 0.464 = \bar{1}.\text{_____} \quad \text{or} \quad 9.\text{_____} - 10$$
$$\log 0.464 = \bar{1}.665 \quad \text{or} \quad 9.665 - 10.$$

(The negative sign is usually written above the characteristic.)

Example 7. Find the log of 0.0002645.

$$\log 0.0002645 = \bar{4}.\text{_____} \quad \text{or} \quad 6.\text{_____} - 10$$
$$\log 0.0002645 = \bar{4}.4216 \quad \text{or} \quad 6.4216 - 10.$$

13.5. *Finding the Logarithm of a Number with Four Significant Digits*

When a number has more than three significant digits its number is not recorded in a four-place table. It may, however, be obtained by *interpolation.*

When this process is used it is assumed that when the number changes there is a corresponding change in the logarithm which is proportional to the change in the number. This assumption is often referred to as the principle of *proportional parts*.

Example 8. Find the log of 86.24.

The mantissa of 8620 is 9355.

The mantissa of 8630 is 9360.

The difference between these two mantissas is 5. Since 8624 is 0.4 of an interval from 8620 to 8630, by the principle of proportional parts we add to 9355

$$0.4 \times 5 = 2,$$

therefore

$$\log 86.24 = 1.9357.$$

Example 9. Find the log of 0.5236.

5230	7185
5240	7193

$0.6 \times 8. = 4.8$

$7185 + 4.8 = 7189.8 = 7190$

$\log 0.5236 = \bar{1}.7190$ or $9.7190 - 10.$

13.6. *Finding the Number Whose Logarithm is Given*

The number of a given logarithm is found by obtaining from a table of logarithms the significant digits corresponding to the mantissa of the logarithm, then determining the position of the decimal point from the characteristic of the logarithm. This procedure is the reverse of finding the logarithm, and, therefore, is often referred to as finding the antilogarithm. (This word is not appropriate for the operation described. The operation is really the reverse of finding the logarithm rather than being opposed as anti-implies.)

Example 10. Find the number whose logarithm is 1.8727.

First find the mantissa 8727 in the table and read the number under N for the first two digits, i.e., 74. The third digit is obtained from the top horizontal row above the 8727, i.e., 6.

Therefore the three digits are 746. Because the characteristic is one the number must have two digits to the left of the decimal point, i.e., 74.6. The reverse of this would be to say that

$$\log 74.6 = 1.8727.$$

Example 11. Find the number whose logarithm is 0.5502.

The three digits are 355. The characteristic is zero, therefore, there should be one digit to the left of the decimal point. The number is 3.55.

The following table summarizes the various characteristics and the placing of the decimal point in the number.

Characteristic	Number (256)
$\bar{3}$ or 7 − 10	.00256
$\bar{2}$ or 8 − 10	.0256
$\bar{1}$ or 9 − 10	.256
0	2.56
1	25.6
2	256

Example 12. Find the number whose logarithm is 9.5026 − 10.

$$\begin{aligned} \log 0.318 &= 9.5024 - 10 \\ \log 0.319 &= \underline{9.5038 - 10} \\ \text{Difference} &= 0.0012 \end{aligned}$$

$$0.5026 - 0.5024 = 0.0002.$$

By the principle of proportional parts the number is

$$\frac{0.0002}{0.0012} \times 0.001 + 0.318 = \frac{2}{12} \times 0.001 + 0.318 = 0.3182.$$

Hence, $\log 0.3182 = 9.5026 - 10$.

13.7. *Multiplication*

To multiply numbers, add their logarithms, then find the number of that logarithm; in general terms:

$$\log ab = \log a + \log b.$$

For example, note the following multiplication:

$$43.3 \times 0.102 \times 0.0530 = ?$$

$$\begin{aligned} \log 43.3 &= 1.6365 \\ \log 0.102 &= 9.0086 - 10 \end{aligned}$$

$$\log 0.0530 = \frac{8.7243 - 10}{19.3694 - 20} \quad \text{or} \quad 9.3694 - 10$$

$$\log 0.234 = 9.3692 - 10$$
$$\log 0.235 = \underline{9.3711 - 10}$$
$$\text{difference} = 0.0019$$

$$0.3694 - 0.3692 = 0.0002$$
$$\tfrac{2}{19} \times 0.001 + 0.234 = 0.2341.$$

Therefore the product is 0.2341.

Because there are three significant digits in each of the numbers the answer should also contain three, i.e., 0.234. As it turned out it was only necessary to determine whether the fourth digit in 0.234 would be greater than 5 or less than 5. If it had been greater than 5, we would round off the number to 0.235.

13.8. *Division*

To divide numbers subtract the log of the numerator by the log of the denominator, then find the number of that logarithm. In general terms $\log (a/b) = \log a - \log b$.

Example 13. $x = 136.3/65.38$

$$\log x = \log 136.3 - \log 65.38$$
$$\log 136.3 = 2.1345$$
$$\log 65.38 = \underline{1.8154}$$
$$\log x = 0.3191$$
$$x = 2.084.$$

It should be obvious that the operations of multiplication and division can be combined.

Example 14. Find $x = \dfrac{17.5 \times 1.92}{0.283 \times 0.0314}$

$$\log x = (\log 17.5 + \log 1.92) - (\log 0.283 + \log 0.0314)$$

$\log 17.5 = 1.2430$	$\log 0.283 \;\;= 9.4518 - 10$
$\log 1.92 = \underline{0.2833}$ (add)	$\log 0.0314 = \underline{8.4969 - 10}$ (add)
1.5263	$17.9487 - 20$
or $\quad 11.5263 - 10$	or $\quad 7.9487 - 10$

$$(11.5263 - 10) - (7.9487 - 10) = 3.5776$$
$$x = 3781.$$

13.9. *Powers*

To raise a number to a given power, multiply the log of the number by the power expressed, then find the number of the logarithm. In eneral terms:

$$\log a^n = n(\log a).$$

Note the following example:

$$\text{Find } x = \sqrt{751} = (751)^{\frac{1}{2}}$$
$$\log x = \tfrac{1}{2}(\log 751)$$
$$\log x = \tfrac{1}{2}(2.8756) = 1.4378$$
$$x = 27.4.$$

13.10. *Applications to Chemistry*

1. *Calculation of* pH

It is more convenient to specify the acidity of a solution as a small number (i.e., 1–14) than to specify it in terms of the hydrogen ion concentration. For this reason the pH of a solution is defined by the equation

$$\text{pH} = -\log [H^+]$$

where $[H^+]$ is the hydrogen ion concentration in units of moles per liter. For a solution whose $[H^+]$ is 1×10^{-4} its pH would be

$$\text{pH} = -\log (1 \times 10^{-4})$$
$$= -\log 1 - \log 10^{-4}$$
$$= -0 + 4$$
$$= 4.$$

2. *Calculation of* $[H^+]$ *Knowing the* pH

The $[H^+]$ may be calculated if one pH is known utilizing the same equation as in part (a) above. For example, to calculate one $[H^+]$ for a solution whose pH is known to be 3.6 proceed as follows:

$$\text{pH} = -\log [H^+]$$
$$3.6 = -\log [H^+]$$
$$\text{or} \quad \log [H^+] = -3.6.$$

It is readily seen that -3.6 is equal to $(-4 + 0.4)$, so we may write

$$\log [H^+] = 0.4 - 4$$
$$[H^+] = \text{antilog of } (0.4) - 4$$
$$[H^+] = (\text{antilog of } 0.4) \times (\text{antilog of } -4)$$
$$[H^+] = 2.5 \times 10^{-4} \text{ moles/liter.}$$

3. *Solubility Product Calculations*

Logarithms are also useful when calculating the molar solubility of a slightly soluble compound such as $Fe(OH)_3$. For example, calculate the molar solubility of $Fe(OH)_3$. The solubility product constant is 1.1×10^{-36}. The equilibrium is

$$Fe(OH)_{3(s)} \rightleftharpoons Fe^{+3} + 3\ OH^-.$$

Let $x = [Fe^{+++}]$, then

$$K_{sp} = x(3x)^3 = 27x^4$$

$$\frac{1.1 \times 10^{-36}}{27} = x^4 = 407 \times 10^{-40}$$

$$x = (407 \times 10^{-40})^{\frac{1}{4}} = (407)^{\frac{1}{4}} \times 10^{-10}.$$

(See Chapter 3 for discussion of exponential numbers.)

The problem is now to determine the value of $(407)^{\frac{1}{4}}$ and we utilize logarithms as follows*:

$$z = (407)^{\frac{1}{4}}$$
$$\log z = \log (407)^{\frac{1}{4}}$$
$$\log z = \tfrac{1}{4} \log 407$$
$$\log z = \tfrac{1}{4} (2.6096) = .6524$$
$$z = \text{antilog } .6524$$
$$z = 4.49 = 4.5$$

$x = [Fe^{+++}] = 4.5 \times 10^{-10}$ moles/liter, the molar solubility of $Fe(OH)_3$.

4. *The Nernst Equation*

Logarithms, of course, can be used by the student whenever confronted with calculations similar to the above. A common problem in electrochemistry is to solve the Nernst equation:

$$E = E^0 - \frac{RT}{nF} 2.303 \log Q$$

---

* This result is only of significance when there are no changes other than the dispersal of the ions.

where

$$E^0 = \text{molar electrode potential}$$
$$n = \text{number electrons involved in the change}$$
$$F = \text{the faraday (96 500 coulombs)}$$
$$Q = \text{ratio of the concentrations}$$
$$R = \text{a constant.}$$

Substituting the numerical values and considering the general equation

$$Red \rightleftharpoons Ox + ne,$$

we have

$$E = E^0 - \frac{(2.303)(8.314)(298)}{n(96\ 500)} \log \frac{[Ox]}{[Red]}$$

$$E = E^0 - \frac{0.0592}{n} \log \frac{[Ox]}{[Red]}.$$

For example, for the half reaction

$$Ce^{+3} \rightleftharpoons Ce^{+4} + e$$

$$E = E^0 - 0.0592 \log \frac{[Ce^{+4}]}{[Ce^{+3}]}$$

and if the concentration of the ions is known, E can be calculated since E^0 is obtained from a table of electrode potentials. If $[Ce^{+4}] = 1M$ and $[Ce^{+3}] = 0.01M$, then

$$E = -1.45 - .0592 \log \frac{1}{10^{-2}}$$

$$E = -1.45 - .0592 \log 100$$
$$E = -1.45 - .0592(2) = 1.57 \text{ V.}$$

The student should observe that if the molar concentrations were one, then

$$E = E^0$$

since

$$\log 1 = 0.$$

Let us consider an overall reaction rather than just one half reaction. In what direction will the following reaction go when the ion concentrations are all 0.1 M?

$$2\ Fe^{++} + I_2 \rightleftharpoons 2\ Fe^{+++} + 2I^-.$$

For

$$2\,Fe^{++} \rightleftharpoons 2\,Fe^{+3} + 2e$$

$$E = E^0 - \frac{0.0592}{2} \log \frac{[Fe^{+3}]^2}{[Fe^{++}]^2}$$

$$E = -0.782 - \frac{0.0592}{2} \log 1$$

$$E = -0.782.$$

For

$$2I^- \rightleftharpoons I_2 + 2e$$

$$E = E^0 - \frac{0.0592}{2} \log \frac{[I_2]}{[I^{-2}]}$$

$$E = -0.535 - 0.0592 \log \frac{1}{0.1}$$

$$E = -0.535 - 0.0592 \log 10$$
$$E = -0.565 \text{ V}.$$

(The concentration of a solid is considered 1 M.)

If the second half reaction is subtracted from the first, the above overall reaction is obtained. Subtracting the two voltages yields the overall voltage

$$E = -0.782 - (-0.565)$$
$$= -0.217 \text{ V}.$$

The negative voltage indicates that the reaction goes to the left as written.

13.11. *Algebra Problems*

Find the characteristic for each of the following numbers:

1. 320	2. 326 000	3. 1006	4. 0.831
5. 0.03	6. 46 000 000	7. 40	8. 1500
9. 0.12	10. 17.28	11. 0.0025	12. 0.00036

Find the mantissa for each of the following numbers:

13. 0.820	14. 935	15. 6.23
16. 256	17. 31.9	18. 493
19. 0.0036	20. 0.000271	21. 1.01

Find the logarithm of each of the following numbers:

22. 728	23. 7.28	24. .728
25. 544	26. 285	27. 965
28. 48.30	29. 5.01	30. 0.261
31. 0.639	32. 0.0533	33. 0.0022
34. 0.000452	35. 49.7	36. 110
37. 8.21	38. 0.571	39. 0.00168

Find the logarithm of each of the following numbers:

40. 5280	41. 9650	42. 1.057
43. 30.84	44. 0.03532	45. 0.0002645
46. 0.4683	47. 0.04683	48. 46.38
49. 1436	50. 49.37	51. 316.2
52. 8.208	53. 110.6	54. 0.5634

Find the number of each of the following logarithms:

55. 3.1568	56. 1.6934	57. 5.6934
58. 2.5000	59. 2.0436	60. 0.9142
61. 0.0008	62. 9.7507	63. $\bar{2}$.0034
64. 7.2006	65. $\bar{1}$.7564	66. $\bar{3}$.7629

Solve for the following using logarithms:

67. $(487)(2.45)(0.0387)$	68. 136.3×65.38
69. $1 \div 22.4$	70. 17.5×28.32
71. $79.28 \div 63.57$	72. $65.38 \div 522.2$
73. $(8.643)^2$	74. $(0.06482)^2$
75. $(72.11)^3$	76. $\sqrt{649}$
77. $3\sqrt{1.92}$	78. 2.54×10^6
79. 2.7×10^{-13}	80. $(5.8 \times 10^{-4})^2$
81. $7.3 \times 10^{-40} \div 1.6 \times 10^{-22}$	82. 0.00166
83. $(573)(966)(0.00841)$	84. $(0.752)(81.3) \div (69.2)$
85. $(152)^3$	86. $\sqrt[4]{0.182}$

13.12. *Chemistry Problems*

Calculate the pH values of solutions with the following H^+ ion concentrations:

1. 10^{-3}	2. 10^{-11}	3. 10^{-14}
4. 4.9×10^{-4}	5. 6.3×10^{-12}	6. 2.4×10^{-10}
7. 1.0×10^{-7}	8. 1.3×10^{-13}	9. 1.3×10^{-5}

Calculate the H^+ ion concentration of solutions with the following pH values:

10. 4.00	11. 3.64	12. 4.25
13. 7.63	14. 13.4	15. 1.23

16. Calculate the molar solubility of each of the following substances from its solubility product constant: $AgBr$, CaF_2, Ag_3PO_4, $Mg(OH)_2$, Ag_2CrO_4, $Pb_3(PO_4)_2$.
17. Calculate the metal ion concentration in a 0.05 M solution of the following complex salts: $Cd(NH_3)_4SO_4$, $Cu(NH_3)_4SO_4$, $Ag(NH_3)_2Cl$, $KAg(CN)_2$, $Na_2Cd(CN)_4$.
18. Calculate the voltage for the half reaction $Cr^{++} \rightleftharpoons Cr^{+3} + e$ when $[Cr^{++}] = 0.001$ M and $[Cr^{+3}] = 1$ M.
19. Determine the voltage for the overall reaction between Sn^{++} and Ce^{+4} and indicate whether the reaction is possible. The ratio of $[Sn^{+4}]/[Sn^{++}] = \frac{1}{4}$ and that $[Ce^{+4}]/[Ce^{+3}] = \frac{1}{2}$.
20. Calculate the voltage for the half reaction $Sn^{++} \rightleftharpoons Sn^{+4} + 2e$ when the concentrations are each 1 M and when $[Sn^{+4}] = 0.1$ M and $[Sn^{++}] = 0.3$ M.

Chapter 14

Natural Logarithms

14.1. Introduction

Natural, or Napierian, logarithms are those which have the number e (2.71828+) for the base. These logarithms play a very important role in mathematics and in certain topics in chemistry. By definition, the natural logarithm of a number x is the exponent in the equation

$$e^y = x \qquad (1)$$

which may be written as

$$y = \ln x.$$

If $y = 0$, $x = 1$ and $\ln 1 = 0$. If $y = 1$, $x = e$ and $\ln e = 1$. As y approaches minus infinity, i.e., $y \to -\infty$, then $x \to 0$ and $\ln 0 = -\infty$.

The student is familiar with the use of tables of common logarithms to the base ten (see Chapter 13). The common logarithm of a number x is the exponent in the equation

$$10^y = x, \qquad (2)$$

or

$$y = \log x.$$

Let us find the relation between $\ln x$ and $\log x$. In equation (1) take the logarithms of both members to the base 10. We have

$$y = \log e = \log x.$$

Solving for y which equals $\ln x$ we obtain the desired relation:

$$\ln x = \frac{\log x}{\log e}. \tag{3}$$

That is, *we obtain the natural logarithm of a number by dividing its common logarithm by log e.* By tables $\log e = 0.4343$ and this number divided into one (i.e., its reciprocal) equals 2.303. Equation (3) may now be written as

$$\ln x = 2.303 \log x.$$

The conversion of one type of logarithm to the other is easily executed.

14.2. *The Logarithmic Curve*

The graph of the equation

$$y = \log_a x, \quad a > 1$$

is called a *logarithmic curve.* As we have already noted a is the base. The two bases in common use are $a = 10$, already discussed, and $a = e = 2.71828^+$, already mentioned.

To draw the graph of

$$y = \log_{10} x$$

we assign to x a series of values and determine the corresponding values of y. For example, when $x = 1$, $y = 0$; $x = 2$, $y = 0.301$; $x = 3$, $y = 0.477$; etc.

To draw the graph of

$$y = \log_e x$$

we first convert the base e to base 10 so that we can use our logarithm table. The conversion factor is 2.303 and

$$y = 2.303 \log_{10} x.$$

We now assign again a series of values to x and determine the corresponding values for y. For example, when $x = 1$, $y = 0$; $x = 2$, $y = 0.692$; $x = 3$, $y = 1.097$; etc.

The data for the equation are plotted in Figure 14.1. Generally, when the equation $y = \log_a x$ is plotted the following are true:

(1) If x approaches zero, $\log x$ decreases without limit. That is, the curve

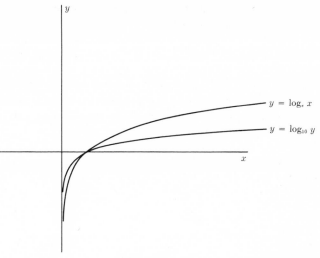

$y = \log_e x$

$y = \log_{10} y$

FIGURE 14.1

approaches the negative end of the y-axis but never touches it. The y-axis is an asymptote in the graph.

(2) If x increases indefinitely, $\log x$ increases without limit. That is, the curve continues to rise above the x-axis with no final value for y.

14.3. The Exponential Curve

An exponential function is an algebraic equation in which the unknown occurs as an exponent, or in an exponent. The graph of the equation

$$y = a^x, \quad a > 1$$

is called an exponential curve. If we solve it for x, we have

$$x = \log_a y.$$

This is the equation of a logarithmic curve with x and y interchanged. On plotting, therefore, you would expect it to differ from the logarithmic curve in that it is placed on the figure so that its position relative to the x- and y-axes is interchanged. For example, in plotting

$$y = a^x$$

we first take the log of both sides to the base 10.

$$\log_{10} y = \log_{10} a^x,$$
$$\log_{10} y = x \log_{10} a.$$

99

Values may then be assigned to y and corresponding values of x determined. The curves for $y = 10^x$ and $y = e^x$ are shown in Figure 14.2.

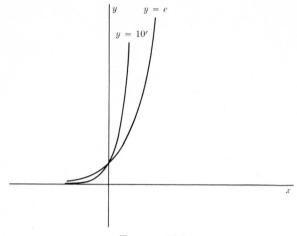

FIGURE 14.2

14.4. *Applications to Chemistry*

1. *Radioactive Decay*

The exponential equation appears in many applications. For example,

(a) The law of the variation of the pressure of the atmosphere with the height above sea level.

(b) The law of cooling of a heated body.

(c) The speed of many chemical reactions.

(d) The rate of decomposition of radium.

Let us examine more closely application (d) above. *Radioactivity* is a property of certain substances in which particles are emitted and the amount of substance decreases (decay). Many substances do this naturally while others may be able to do this after some external influence has been applied.

A substance decays according to a logarithmic process which is described by the equation

$$\log_e \frac{C_0}{C} = kt$$

$$\text{or} \quad 2.303 \log_{10} \frac{C_0}{C} = kt,$$

$$\log \frac{C_0}{C} = \frac{kt}{2.303} \tag{4}$$

where C_0 is the amount of substance at the beginning of the decay, C is the amount of substance after time t has elapsed, and k is the decay constant.

The time required for one-half of the substance to decay (or disappear) is called the half-life of that substance. The half-life $(t_{\frac{1}{2}})$ may be obtained from (1) by putting $C = \frac{1}{2}C_0$ and solving for $t_{\frac{1}{2}}$.

$$\log \frac{C_0}{\frac{1}{2}C_0} = \frac{kt_{\frac{1}{2}}}{2.303}$$

$$\frac{2.303 \log 2}{k} = t_{\frac{1}{2}}$$

$$\frac{0.693}{k} = t_{\frac{1}{2}}. \tag{5}$$

It is meaningless to speak of the time necessary for all the material to decompose because, theoretically, an infinite time is required.

Radioactive decay is a process in which the emission of a particle (s) decreases in an exponential (logarithmic) manner, as shown in Figure 14.3.

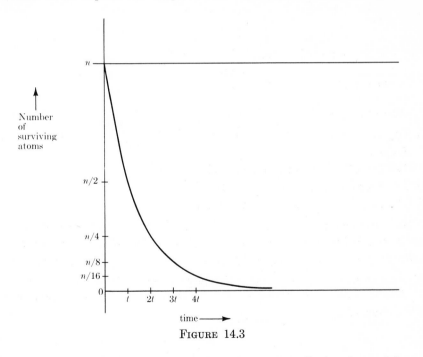

FIGURE 14.3

Equation (1), which is a logarithmic function, can easily be changed into an exponential function:

$$C_0/C = 10^{kt/2.303}.$$

When one uses a counting device such as the Geiger counter, the counting rate or "activity" is proportional to the decay rate of the sample and (1) can be modified to

$$\log \frac{A_0}{A} = \frac{kt}{2.303} \qquad (6)$$

where A_0 is the initial activity and A is the activity after time t, and the exponential function modified to

$$\frac{A_0}{A} = 10^{kt/2.303}.$$

This is the method used for obtaining the decay constant (k) of such substances as uranium and radium. The decay constant is a distinguishing characteristic of a radioactive substance.

Example 1. A radioactive substance has a half-life of 2 days. The count is 1000 counts/min (as measured with a Geiger counter) at some particular time. What is its count 2 days later? (k for the substance is 0.301.) Use equation (3).

$$\log \frac{1000}{A} = \frac{0.346 \times 2}{2.303}$$

$$\log \frac{1000}{A} = 0.301$$

$$\log 1000 - \log A = 0.301$$
$$- \log A = 0.301 - \log 1000$$
$$- \log A = 0.301 - 3.000$$
$$- \log A = -2.699$$
$$- \log A = 2.699$$
$$A = 500 \text{ counts/min.}$$

Example 2. Immediately after an atomic explosion the strontium-90 count is known to be 2000 counts/min. What will be the count 10 years after the explosion? ($t_{\frac{1}{2}} = 25$ yrs., $k = 0.267$ yrs^{-1})

$$\log \frac{2000}{A} = \frac{0.0276 \times 10}{2.303}$$

$$\log \frac{2000}{A} = 0.120$$

$$\log 2000 - \log A = 0.120$$
$$\log A = \log 2000 - 0.120$$
$$\log A = 3.301 - 0.120 = 3.181$$
$$A = 1517 \text{ counts/min.}$$

The 2000 counts/min was hypothetical and the original count will, of course, depend upon the size of the bomb. The point is that when a substance has a long half-life it takes a long time before it decays and is no longer radio-active, or for all practical purposes has no activity.

2. *Arrhenius Equation*

It has long been known as an empirical fact that many reactions near room temperature (25°C) double or treble their velocity for every 10° rise in temperature. Arrhenius proposed the following more quantitative relation:

$$k = se^{-Ea/RT}$$

where k is the specific reaction rate, s is a constant, E_a is heat of activation, and R is the gas constant.

If the equation is set in logarithmic form, we have

$$\ln k = \frac{-E_a}{R}\frac{1}{T} + \ln s,$$

$$\log k = \frac{-E_a}{2.3R}\frac{1}{T} + \frac{\log s}{2.3}.$$

This is often written as

$$\log k = \frac{-E_a}{2.3R}\frac{1}{T} + \text{const},$$

since the logarithm of a constant is a constant, and a constant divided by a constant is still a constant.

14.5. *Algebra Problems*

Solve the following by inspection:

1. $5^x = 25$ 2. $3^x = 27$ 3. $5^x = 125$
4. $2^{x-1} = 32$ 5. $3^{x-2} = 81$ 6. $5^{x+1} = 25$
7. $3^x = \frac{1}{9}$ 8. $9^x = 3$ 9. $16^x = \frac{1}{4}$

Solve the following by logarithms (refer to Chapter 13 if necessary).

10. $z^x = 24$ 11. $3^x = 17$ 12. $5^x = 116$
13. $z^{x-1} = 52$ 14. $3^{x-2} = 80$ 15. $5^{x+1} = 36$
16. $1.08^y = 1.26$ 17. $1.09^y = 1.27$ 18. $1.10^y = 3$

Solve the following for the letter indicated:

19. $x = a^y$; y 20. $x = ay^m$; m 21. $x = 5^y$; y
22. $x = 3y^m$; m 23. $z = 8^x$; x 24. $x = 3x_0^m$; m
25. $m = m_0e^t$; t (use base e)   26. $n = n_0e^{ht}$; t (use base e)
27. $m = m_0e^{-t}$; t (use base e)

Plot the graphs of the following equations:

28. $y = 8^x$ 29. $y = 15^x$ 30. $y = 10e^x$

31. $x = 10^y$ 32. $y = e^{-x}$ 33. $y = \log x$

34. $y = \log_e x$ 35. $y = \log 5x$ 36. $y = \log (1/x)$

14.6. Chemistry Problems

1. A first-order reaction (one in which the rate of reaction is found by experiment to be directly proportional to the concentration of the reacting substance) is described, in terms of concentration and time, by

$$-\ln C_A = kt + \text{const.}$$

Convert the equation to common logarithms. What kind of plot is produced when the logarithm of the concentration is plotted against time?

2. Another equation that represents a first-order reaction is

$$k = \frac{2.303}{t} \log \frac{C_0}{C}.$$

Put the equation into the exponential forms.

3. Using the equation given in Problem 2, determine t for a first-order reaction after one half of the original substance has reacted. (Find simplest equation possible.)

4. When the rate of a reaction is proportional to the concentration of the two reacting substances, $(A + B \rightarrow AB)$, the reaction is of the second order. If the reacting substances have initial molar concentrations represented by a and b $(a \neq b)$, then these concentrations are related to time by

$$kt = \frac{1}{a - b} \ln \frac{b(a - x)}{a(b - x)}$$

when $k =$ proportionality factor and x denotes the number of moles of A or B in each liter reacting in time t. Solve the equation for k and put in the simplest logarithmic form. What can you plot to obtain a straight line?

5. In the logarithmic form of the Arrhenius equation, what do you plot to get a straight line? What represents the slope of the line? (See Section 7.6, 10.)

6. In the equation given in Problem 5, the value of s for many unimolecular gas reactions is 1×10^{13}. Place this value in the equation and obtain its logarithmic form.

7. Calculate the Arrhenius activation energy for the decomposition

$$N_2O_5 \rightleftharpoons 2NO_2 + \tfrac{1}{2}O_2$$

if, at 35°C, $k = 1.35 \times 10^{-4}$ sec $^{-1}$.

8. The electromotive force of a cell is given by

$$E = E^0 - \frac{RT}{nF} \ln \frac{[\text{Products}]}{[\text{Reactants}]}.$$

Put the equation in logarithmic form and simplify as much as possible assuming $n = 1$. (See Section 13.10, 4.)

9. Calculate the emf (E) of the following cell at 25°C:

$$\text{Sn} \mid \text{Sn}^{++}(0.6 \text{ M}) \parallel \text{Pb}^{++}(0.3 \text{ M}) \mid \text{Pb},$$

the cell reaction is

$$\text{Sn} + \text{Pb}^{++} \rightleftharpoons \text{Sn}^{++} + \text{Pb}.$$

(The symbol $\parallel$ indicates a salt bridge; a single vertical indicates a contact between two different phases—the solution of the ion and the solid.)

10. Determine the emf (E) of the following cell at a temperature of 25°C:

$$\text{Zn} \mid \text{Zn}^{++}(3 \text{ M}) \parallel \text{Cu}^{++}(10^{-4} \text{ M}) \mid \text{Cu}.$$

Chapter 15

Significant Figures

15.1. *Scientific Measurement*

One way that the scientist makes the physical world intelligible is to make measurements. The more accurate the measurement the more that is known about some particular object. Measurement, of course, is not restricted to the physical and natural sciences. The psychologist and the educationist also measure and attempt to use it in predicting a person's future behavior. For example, in the field of education, a person's I.Q. is determined, which is helpful (along with other information) to predict his future success in school. In this area of human measurement prophecy is difficult because of so many variables which are involved, i.e., environment, motivation, etc.

It is not intended to be implied that there are no problems in physical science measurement; there is no doubt that this type of measurement has been developed to a high degree of refinement. The scientist realizes that the process of measuring necessarily involves a mutual interaction between the object to be measured and the measuring device, and that this must, to a certain degree, change the measured object. For example, in using a wire gauge to measure the diameter of a wire, the instrument causes a slight deformation of the wire and a slight error is thereby introduced. The diameter could be measured under a microscope, but now the wire must be illuminated with light which heats the wire and makes it expand, thus introducing an error. It is evident that there are errors in physical measurements. The accuracy of a measurement has a natural limit which is imposed both by the instrument and the object being measured.

The same difficulty also occurs when using glass apparatus. A 10 ml pipette, for example, will deliver a little more or less depending upon the amount of heat which either expands or contracts the glass. This error is largely avoided by using the pipette under the conditions in which it was standardized.

The numerical value of every observed measurement is, therefore, an approximation. That is, it is impossible for the result of any measurement to be mathematically exact. All that a measurement or a series of measurements can demonstrate is that there is a certain probability that the true magnitude will lie within certain limits. The verb "to equal" in the sciences does not have the exactness that it has in mathematics. A measurement in the sciences for which the error was entirely unknown would be quite meaningless. For example, a series of weighings of a crucible would never indicate that the weight was, say, exactly 100 gm, and to write weight of crucible = 100 gm would be very misleading. If weighed on an analytical balance it would indicate that the true weight lies within the limits 100.0001 to 99.9999 gm. The measurement indicates, then, the probability that the true weight falls within these limits.

In chemistry measurements it is necessary to know how reliable a measurement is, i.e., how many digits (figures) are *significant*. The *degree of certainty* in any physical measurement is reflected in the number of significant figures recorded. It is a clear indication of the accuracy of the equipment, experimental method, and observation. Any recorded measurement should contain only reliable digits with the last reliable digit being less reliable.

A 500 ml graduated cylinder, precise to 2 ml, is used to measure a volume of water and the measurement is recorded at 378 ml. The number has three significant figures with the third one not as reliable as the first two. If we wish to give a more precise meaning to the third figure we could write the number as 378 ± 2 ml. So that the true value lies somewhere between 376 and 380 ml.

15.2. *Identifying Figures*

The number of significant figures in a number is seen in the following:

0.54	···	2	24.38	··· 4
7.25	···	3	72501	··· 5.
1.09	···	3		

When a zero occurs in a number it is significant only if it occurs between any two digits other than zero, or to the right of a number beyond the decimal point. For example, the zeros in 406.6, 820.3, 300.4 are significant.

A zero, though, is not significant if it is used to fix the decimal point. For example, the zero in 0.033 is not significant. If the number referred to a measurement of say 0.033 m, then we could also write it as 3.3 cm. In either case there are two significant figures.

It is possible to use exponential numbers as a way of avoiding ambiguity. For example, there are three significant digits in 96 500. This becomes obvious if the number is written as 9.56×10^4.

15.3. *Application to Addition and Subtraction*

No more figures should be used than are reliable. In a set of numbers being added or subtracted, the number with the fewest reliable figures determines the resulting number. For example, consider the following addition:

$$
\begin{array}{r}
20.0 \quad \text{m} \\
281. \quad \text{m} \\
\underline{1.256\ \text{m}} \\
302.256\ \text{m} = 302\ \text{m}.
\end{array}
$$

The result is expressed to the nearest meter since 281 is expressed only to the nearest meter. The 2 in 302 is not changed since 1.256 is smaller than 0.5. See Section 15.5 for a discussion of rounding numbers.

Now let us consider the following subtraction:

$$
\begin{array}{r}
23.76 \quad \text{ml} \\
- \quad 6.812\ \text{ml} \\
\hline
16.948\ \text{ml} = 16.95\ \text{ml}.
\end{array}
$$

There are four significant figures in each number and the result should have four. The 23.76 is known to the nearest hundredth of a milliliter and the result, therefore, should be expressed to the nearest hundredth of a milliliter.

15.4. *Application to Multiplication and Division*

In multiplying and dividing the result can have no more significant figures than the least reliable quantity. When multiplying or dividing 8.584 and 1.68, for example, the answer should be given in three significant figures.

$$
(8.584)(1.68) = 14.4
$$
$$
8.584 \div 1.68 = 5.109 = 5.11.
$$

15.5. *Rounding Numbers*

In the above problem 5.109 was changed to 5.11. The process of changing the number is called "rounding off" and its purpose is to obtain an answer with the proper number of significant figures. In rounding numbers use the following rules:

1. When the first digit dropped on the right is greater than five, increase the last remaining digit by one. Thus in 5.109 the nine is dropped and the zero is changed to one.
2. When the first digit dropped is less than five, the last remaining digit remains unchanged.
3. When the first digit dropped is five and there are no digits after it, the last digit remaining is changed to an even number. For example, 3485 and 3475 are both changed to 348. If the first digit dropped is five and there are other digits to the right of it, increase the last remaining digit by one.

15.6. *Significant Figures and Exponential Notation*

The number of significant figures is not related to the position of the decimal point. That is, the same number of significant figures are required whether we express an area as 12 030 mm² or as 0.1203 m². It is not certain whether the last zero in the area expressed in millimeters is significant. This uncertainty can be avoided if the numbers are written in exponential form. (See Chapter 4 for a discussion of exponential numbers.) In the first case we have

$$1.203 \times 10^4 \text{ mm}^2$$

and in the second

$$1.203 \times 10^{-2} \text{ m}^2.$$

There are four significant figures in each case.

15.7. *Summary*

The above are approximate rules which will be helpful in doing many chemistry problems. The proper use of significant figures depends many times on common sense. The student should try to avoid the use of too many figures. It is interesting to note that the very use of the decimal notation (i.e., 1.635) implies that it would be impossible to know the number exactly since it would require an infinite number of figures after the decimal point to express the quantity exactly. In mathematics, though, a simple fraction ($\frac{3}{2}$) is commonly used to represent a mathematically exact quantity.

15.8. *Problems*

Determine the number of significant figures in the following:

1. 584 gm   *3*   2. 4.4 lb   *2*   3. 5.202 lb   *4*

4. 0.3739 in. *4*   5. 0.0533 mi *3*   6. 2.0040 kg *4*

7. 15.0 ml *2*   8. 3.9×10^{-7} cm *2*   9. 8.112×10^3 gm *4*

Add the following:

10. 0.77 gm, 8 gm, 203 gm   11. 25.481 m, 2.71 m, 6.0 m

12. 0.522 l, 0.092 l, 0.0054 l

Subtract the following:

13. 2.76 lb, 0.3 lb   14. 462.5 ft, 18.7 ft   15. 43 gm, 0.3 gm

Multiply the following:

16. 2.13×0.4 17. 4.04×2.113

18. 808.17×0.160 19. 42.7×0.048

20. 0.023×2.8 21. $(8.8 \times 10^4)(2.44 \times 10^5)$

Divide the following:

22. $25.79 \div 4.25$ 23. $82.14 \div 0.417$

24. $0.023 \div 0.008$ 25. $2.8 \div 0.0023$

Chapter 16

Solving Problems

16.1. *The Value of Algebraic Notation in Physics and Chemistry*

To see the value of algebraic notation consider, for example, the familiar formula $S = \frac{1}{2}gt^2$. Translating this formula into words, we say the distance through which a body will fall from rest under the influence of gravity equals the product of one half of the acceleration of gravity and the square of the number of seconds.

When one becomes accustomed to it, he can think distance easier and more quickly from seeing S rather than from seeing the words "distance a body falls through in t seconds." This explains in part why the algebraic notation is so valuable in all kinds of scientific work.

16.2. *Applications to Chemistry*

1. *Boyle's Law*

If the air is contained in a vessel of volume V under pressure of P lbs. per sq. in., Boyle's Law states that the product of volume and pressure equals a constant number C. Express this truth algebraically.

$$PV = C.$$

16.3. *Density*

If D, V, W represent the density, volume, and weight of one kind of metal, and D_1, V_1, and W the density, volume, and weight of an equal weight of another, find V_1 in terms of D, V, and D_1.

$$D = W/V,$$
$$W = DV,$$
and
$$W = D_1V_1.$$

Therefore,

$$DV = D_1V_1$$
and
$$V_1 = DV/D_1.$$

16.4. Charles' Law

A gas contracts $\frac{1}{273}$ of its zero Centigrade volume for each degree drop of temperature. Find the volume of the gas V_t in terms of its volume at $0°$ Centigrade V_0 and the temperature t.

$$V_t = V_0 - \frac{t}{273} V_0.$$

16.5. Other Types of Problems and Their Solution

There are two parts to the solution of a problem in algebra: the *statement*, or construction of the equation of equations and the *solution* of the equation or equations.

In the solution of a problem, four steps may be described:

(a) Reading the problem carefully, getting all its conditions in mind, and letting a letter, or letters, represent its unknown number or numbers.
(b) Constructing the expression(s) involving the unknown(s).
(c) Constructing equation(s) with the expressions that are equal to each other.
(d) Solving the equation(s) and verifying the answer(s).

Example 1. One base angle of an isosceles triangle is three times as great as the vertical angle. Find the number of degrees in each, knowing that the sum of all three angles is $180°$.

Let $x =$ the number of degrees in the vertical angle.
Then $3x =$ the number of degrees in each base angle.
Now

$$x + 3x + 3x = 180$$
$$7x = 180$$
$$x = \tfrac{180}{7} = 25\tfrac{5}{7}.$$

Example 2. A rectangle has its length 3 feet greater than its width. If the length is increased by 4 feet and the width by one foot, the area of the new rectangle will be 3 times the area of the old. What are the length and width of the original rectangle?

$$\text{Let } x = \text{width}$$
$$\text{then } 3x = \text{length.} \quad \text{(original rectangle)}$$

$$\text{Let } x + 1 = \text{width}$$
$$3x + 4 = \text{length} \quad \text{(new rectangle)}$$

$$\text{(area of new rectangle)} = 3\text{(area of old rectangle)}$$
$$(x + 1)(3x + 4) = 3(x)(3x)$$
$$3x^2 + 7x + 4 = 9x^2$$
$$6x^2 - 7x - 4 = 0.$$

The student should consult Chapter 10 for a discussion of the solution of quadratic equations.

Example 3. A grocer has two kinds of kerosene oil, one worth 12 cents, the other 15 cents a gallon. How many gallons of each will he take to make a mixture of 55 gallons worth $7.20?

$$\text{Let } x = \text{number of gallons of 15 cent oil}$$
$$\text{then } 55 - x = \text{number of gallons of 12 cent oil.}$$

Now
$$15x + 12(55 - x) = 720$$
$$15x + 660 - 12x = 720$$
$$3x = 60$$
$$x = 20.$$

Therefore, the grocer will use 20 gallons of the 15 cent oil and 35 gallons of the 12 cent oil. This is verified by substituting into the equation

$$15(20) + 12(55 - 20) = 720$$
$$300 + 12(35) = 720$$
$$720 = 720.$$

Example 4. How many gallons of a mixture containing 75% alcohol should be added to 5 gallons of a 30% solution to give a 40% solution?

Let x = number of gallons of 75% solution and the final volume = $5 + x$. (alcohol in the 75% solution) + (alcohol in the 30% solution) = (alcohol in the 40% solution)

$$0.75x + 0.30 \ (5) = 0.40 \ (5 + x)$$
$$0.75x + 1.50 = 2.00 + 0.40x$$
$$0.35x = 0.50$$

$$x = \frac{0.50}{0.35} = \frac{50}{35} = 1.42 \text{ gallons.}$$

16.6. *Problems*

1. Find the distance a body falls in 5 sec. Take $g = 32.15$.
2. A stone fell from a balloon a mile high. How many seconds elapsed before it reached the earth?
3. The moment of a force, or torque, is measured by the product of the magnitude of the force (f) and the perpendicular distance (d) from the axis of rotation to the line of action of the force. Express the moment (m) in algebraic notation.
4. A couple consists of two oppositely directed forces that produce rotation. A couple can be balanced by another couple of equal moment. Express this equality by an algebraic notation.
5. A force (or weight) of 20 lbs balances a weight of 36 lbs at the extremities of a weightless lever 14 in. long. Compute the lengths of the arms. (Problems 3 and 4 should be done first.)
6. What is the moment of a couple that has 9 lbs of force directed in opposite directions and separated by 4 ft?
7. The average speed of a body is the distance covered d divided by the time t taken to cover this distance. If the speed of a body is increasing or decreasing at a uniform rate, then the average speed is the sum of the final speed V_2 and the initial speed V_1 divided by 2. Express both in algebraic notation.
8. A train's speed increases uniformly from 30 mph to 60 mph in 5 min. Determine the average speed.
9. Acceleration a is the change in velocity divided by the time taken for the change. Express in algebraic notation.
10. Calculate the acceleration for Problem 8.
11. A body moves from rest with an acceleration of 20 cm/sec². Determine the time required to gain a speed of 70 cm/sec.
12. A force F acting on a body is equal to the product of the mass m of the body and its acceleration a. Express in algebraic notation.
13. A 20 gm body is acted on by a force of 30 dynes. Determine the acceleration of the body. 1 dyne = 1 gm cm/sec².
14. The momentum M of a body is equal to the product of its mass m and its velocity v. Express in algebraic notation.
15. The impulse j, application of force to a body, is equal to the product of the force F applied and the length of time t the force acts. Express in algebraic notation.
16. The change in momentum by an impulse is numerically equal to the impulse. The change in momentum is given by the product of mass of the body and the difference in the initial velocity u and the final velocity v. Express in algebraic notation.

17. An 8 gm bullet is fired horizontally into a 9 kg block of wood which is free to move. The velocity of the block and bullet after impact is 40 cm/sec. Calculate the initial velocity of the bullet.
18. The density d of a body is equal to its mass m per unit volume v. Express in algebraic notation.
19. The specific gravity of a body is its density d_b divided by the density of water d_w. Express in algebraic notation.
20. Determine the volume in gallons of 400 lbs of cottonseed oil of sp. gr. 0.926. One gallon of water weighs 8.34 lbs.
21. Boyle's Law. At constant temperature the product of the initial pressure P_1 and volume V_1 equals the product of the final pressure P_2 and volume V_2. Express in algebraic notation.
22. A mass of oxygen occupies 5.00 l under a pressure of 740 mm of Hg. Determine the volume of the same mass of gas at 760 mm of Hg, the temperature remaining constant.
23. Charles' Law. At constant pressure the quotient of the initial volume V_1 and temperature T_1 equals the quotient of the final volume V_2 and the temperature T_2. Express in algebraic notation.
24. A mass of neon occupies 200 l at 373°K. Find its volume at 373°K. (The temperature must be expressed in degrees Kelvin which is °C + 273.)

In the following be sure to state exactly what your letter(s) represent, including the units of measurement, if any.

25. If five is added to a certain number, we get 20. Find the number.
26. A certain number is 4 more than another number, and their sum is 25. Find the numbers.
27. The sum of three consecutive even integers is 84. Find the integers.
28. The larger of two numbers exceeds the smaller by 4. If the sum of the numbers is 56, what are the numbers?
29. A boatman who can row 5 mph in still water rows a certain distance upstream and back in 4 hr. How many miles upstream does he go if the stream itself flows 3 m in 2 hr? (Time = distance/speed.)
30. One man can do a job in 5 days and another can do it in 7 days. How long would it take if they worked together? Hint: Let x = number of days it takes them to do the job working together.
31. How much cream which is 30% butterfat must be taken with milk which is 3% butterfat in order to have 540 lbs which is 4.5% butterfat? Hint: Let x = number of lbs of cream.
32. How much water must be added to 50 ml of 90% alcohol by volume to dilute it to 65% alcohol by volume?
33. A company that manufactures fertilizer wants to blend 18¢ per lb fertilizer with 750 lbs of fertilizer worth 8¢ per lb to make a mixture worth 12¢ per lb. How many lbs of the 18¢ fertilizer should the company use?
34. A man walks at a rate of 5 mph to a destination and then rides back at a rate of 35 mph. The round trip took 4 hours. How far did he walk?
35. The edges of two cubes differ by 2 in., and their volumes differ by 728 cu. in. Find the length of the edge in both cubes.
36. The perimeter of one square is 20 in. longer than that of another, and its area

exceeds two times that of the other by 25 sq. in. Find the length of the side of each square.

37. An investor bought 40 shares on one stock at $4.80 per share and a certain number of shares at $2.00. How many shares of $2.00 stock did he buy if he had paid an average of $3.00 per share?

38. A car goes 10 mph faster than a bus and requires 2 hours less time to travel 300 miles. Find the rate of each.

APPENDIX I

1. Greek Alphabet
2. Common Abbreviations
3. Physical–Chemical Constants
4. Metric Units and Conversion Factors
5. Atomic Weights

1. Greek Alphabet

letters		names	letters		names	letters		names
A	α	Alpha	I	ι	Iota	P	ρ	Rho
B	β	Beta	K	κ	Kappa	Σ	$\sigma\ s$	Sigma
Γ	γ	Gamma	Λ	λ	Lambda	T	τ	Tau
Δ	δ	Delta	M	μ	Mu	Υ	υ	Upsilon
E	ϵ	Epsilon	N	ν	Nu	Φ	ϕ	Phi
Z	ζ	Zeta	Ξ	ξ	Xi	X	χ	Chi
H	η	Eta	O	o	Omicron	Ψ	ψ	Psi
Θ	θ	Theta	Π	π	Pi	Ω	ω	Omega

2. Common Abbreviations

$\overset{\circ}{\text{A}}$	angstrom unit	ν	frequency of radiation
emf	electromotive force	E	activation energy; voltage
K	equilibrium constant; absolute temperature	F	faraday
		K_b	boiling point constant
K_d	dissociation constant	K_h	hydrolysis constant
K_i	ionization constant	K_{sp}	solubility product constant
M	molecular weight	N	Avogadro's number
R	ideal gas constant	T	absolute temperature
V	volume	D	density
e	electron; electronic charge	h	Planck's constant
k	specific rate constant	m	molality
n	number of moles	p	pressure
pH	measure of concentration of hydrogen ion in solution	λ	wavelength of radiation

3. Table of Physical-Chemical Constants

Volume of ideal gas at 0°C, one standard
atmosphere   22 414 liters/mole

117

One calorie (defined)   4.1840 absolute joules
Gas constant per mole   1.987 cal/degree/mole; 0.082
                                          liter-atm/degree/mole
Faraday constant   96 496 coul/gram equivalent
Avogadro's number 6.02×10^{23}/mole
Angstrom unit 10^{-8} cm
Pressure (1 atm)   760 mm of Hg; 29.92 in. of Hg
Absolute zero (0°K) $-273°C$

4. Metric Units and Conversion Factors

Weight:
   1 kilogram (kg) = 1000 grams (gm)
   1 gram = 1000 milligrams (mg)

Length:
   1 meter (m) = 100 centimeters (cm)
   1 centimeter = 10 millimeters (mm)

Volume:
   1 liter (l) = 1000 milliliters (ml)
   1000 milliliters = 1000.028 cubic centimeters (cm³)

Weight:
   1 pound = 454 grams
   1 kilogram = 2.20 pounds

Length:
   1 inch = 2.54 centimeters
   1 meter = 39.4 inches
   1 kilometer = 0.62 miles

Volume:
   1 quart = 946 milliliters
   1 liter = 1.06 quarts

Length:
   1 Angstrom unit (Å) = 10^{-8} centimeter
   1 micron = 10^{-3} millimeter

Volume:
   1 cubic foot = 28.3 liters
               = 7.48 gallons
   1 ounce (US liquid) = 29.6 milliliters

Mass:
   1 gram = 15.4 grains
   1 ounce (avoirdupois) = 28.3 grams
   1 ounce (apothecary, troy) = 31.1 grams

Pressure:
   1 atmosphere (atm)
      = pressure of a mercury column
         760 mm or 29.92 inches high
      = 14.696 lb per sq. in.
      = 1.0133 bars (dynes per cm²)
      = 1033.3 grams per cm²

5. Table of Atomic Weights (Based on Carbon-12)

	Symbol	Atomic Number	Atomic Weight		Symbol	Atomic Number	Atomic Weight
Actinium	Ac	89	(227)	Barium	Ba	56	137.34
Aluminum	Al	13	26.9815	Berkelium	Bk	97	(247)
Americium	Am	95	(243)	Beryllium	Be	4	9.0122
Antimony	Sb	51	121.75	Bismuth	Bi	83	208.980
Argon	Ar	18	39.948	Boron	B	5	10.811
Arsenic	As	33	74.922	Bromine	Br	35	79.909
Astatine	At	85	(210)	Cadmium	Cd	48	112.40

	Symbol	Atomic Number	Atomic Weight *or Mass*		Symbol	Atomic Number	Atomic Weight
Calcium	Ca	20	40.08	Nitrogen	N	7	14.0067
Californium	Cf	98	(251)	Nobelium	No	102	(254)
Carbon	C	6	12.0111	Osmium	Os	76	190.2
Cerium	Ce	58	140.12	Oxygen	O	8	15.9994
Cesium	Cs	55	132.905	Palladium	Pd	46	106.4
Chlorine	Cl	17	35.453	Phosphorus	P	15	30.9738
Chromium	Cr	24	51.996	Platinum	Pt	78	195.09
Cobalt	Co	27	58.933	Plutonium	Pu	94	(242)
Copper	Cu	29	63.54	Polonium	Po	84	(210)
Curium	Cm	96	(247)	Potassium	K	19	39.102
Dysprosium	Dy	66	162.50	Praseodymium	Pr	59	140.907
Einsteinium	Es	99	(254)	Promethium	Pm	61	(147)
Erbium	Er	68	167.26	Protoactinium	Pa	91	(231)
Europium	Eu	63	151.96	Radium	Ra	88	(226)
Fermium	Fm	100	(253)	Radon	Rn	86	(222)
Fluorine	F	9	18.9984	Rhenium	Re	75	186.2
Francium	Fr	87	(223)	Rhodium	Rh	45	102.905
Gadolinium	Gd	64	157.25	Rubidium	Rb	37	85.47
Gallium	Ga	31	69.72	Ruthenium	Ru	44	101.07
Germanium	Ge	32	72.59	Samarium	Sm	62	150.35
Gold	Au	79	196.967	Scandium	Sc	21	44.956
Hafnium	Hf	72	178.49	Selenium	Se	34	78.96
Helium	H	2	4.0026	Silicon	Si	14	28.086
Holmium	Ho	67	164.930	Silver	Ag	47	107.870
Hydrogen	H	1	1.00797	Sodium	Na	11	22.9898
Indium	In	49	114.82	Strontium	Sr	38	87.62
Iodine	I	53	126.904	Sulfur	S	16	32.064
Iridium	Ir	77	192.2	Tantalum	Ta	73	180.948
Iron	Fe	26	55.847	Technetium	Tc	43	(99)
Krypton	Kr	36	83.80	Tellurium	Te	52	127.60
Lanthanum	La	57	138.91	Terbium	Tb	65	158.924
Lawrencium	Lw	103	(257)	Thallium	Tl	81	204.37
Lead	Pb	82	207.19	Thorium	Th	90	232.038
Lithium	Li	3	6.939	Thulium	Tm	69	168.934
Lutetium	Lu	71	174.97	Tin	Sn	50	118.69
Magnesium	Mg	12	24.312	Titanium	Ti	22	47.90
Manganese	Mn	25	54.938	Tungsten	W	74	183.85
Mendelevium	Md	101	(256)	Uranium	U	92	238.03
Mercury	Hg	80	200.59	Vanadium	V	23	50.942
Molybdenum	Mo	42	95.94	Xenon	Xe	54	131.30
Neodymium	Nd	60	144.24	Ytterbium	Yb	70	173.04
Neon	Ne	10	20.183	Yttrium	Y	39	88.905
Neptunium	Np	93	(237)	Zinc	Zn	30	65.37
Nickel	Ni	28	58.71	Zirconium	Zr	40	91.22
Niobium	Nb	41	92.906				

APPENDIX II

1. Vapor Pressure of Water
2. Ionization Constants of Weak Electrolytes
3. Dissociation Constants of Complex Ions
4. Solubility Product Constants
5. Oxidation–Reduction Potentials

1. *Vapor Pressure of Water*

Temperature (0°C)	Pressure (mm Hg)	Temperature (0°C)	Pressure (mm Hg)
0.0	4.58	20.0	17.54
1.0	4.93	21.0	18.65
2.0	5.29	22.0	19.83
3.0	5.69	23.0	21.07
4.0	6.10	24.0	22.38
5.0	6.54	25.0	23.76
6.0	7.01	26.0	25.21
7.0	7.51	27.0	26.74
8.0	8.05	28.0	28.35
9.0	8.61	29.0	30.04
10.0	9.21	30.0	31.82
11.0	9.84	35.0	42.18
12.0	10.52	40.0	55.32
13.0	11.23	45.0	71.88
14.0	11.99	50.0	92.51
15.0	12.79	60.0	149.4
16.0	13.63	70.0	233.7
17.0	14.53	80.0	355.1
18.0	15.48	90.0	525.8
19.0	16.48	100.0	760.0

2. *Ionization Constants of Weak Electrolytes*

Acid		K_a
Acetic	$HC_2H_3O_2$	1.8×10^{-5}
Arsenic	H_3AsO_4	$K_1 \quad 5 \times 10^{-3}$
	$H_2AsO_4^-$	$K_2 \ 8.3 \times 10^{-8}$
	$HAsO_4^{-2}$	$K_3 \quad 1 \times 10^{-12}$
Hydrated aluminum ion	$Al(H_2O)_n^{+3}$	$K_1 \ 1.2 \times 10^{-5}$
Benzoic	$HC_7H_5O_2$	6.5×10^{-5}
Carbonic	H_2CO_3	$K_1 \ 4.2 \times 10^{-7}$
	HCO_3^-	$K_2 \ 4.8 \times 10^{-11}$
Cyanic	$HCNO$	2.0×10^{-4}
Formic	$HCHO_2$	2.1×10^{-4}
Hydrazoic	HN_3	2.0×10^{-5}
Hydrocyanic	HCN	4.0×10^{-10}
Hydrofluoric	HF	7.0×10^{-4}
Hydrogen peroxide	H_2O_2	2.4×10^{-12}
Hydrogen sulfide	H_2S	$K_1 \ 1.0 \times 10^{-7}$
	HS^-	$K_2 \ 1.2 \times 10^{-15}$
Hypobromous	$HBrO$	2.0×10^{-9}
Hypochlorous	$HClO$	3.5×10^{-8}
Nitrous	HNO_2	4.4×10^{-4}
Oxalic	$H_2C_2O_4$	$K_1 \ 4.5 \times 10^{-2}$
	$HC_2O_4^-$	$K_2 \ 5.5 \times 10^{-5}$
Phenol	HC_6H_5O	1×10^{-10}
Phosphoric	H_3PO_4	$K_1 \ 7.5 \times 10^{-3}$
	$H_2PO_4^-$	$K_2 \ 6.2 \times 10^{-8}$
	HPO_4^{-2}	$K_3 \quad 1 \times 10^{-12}$
Phosphorous	H_3PO_3	$K_1 \quad 2 \times 10^{-2}$
	$H_2PO_3^-$	$K_2 \quad 6 \times 10^{-7}$
Propionic	$HC_3H_5O_2$	1.3×10^{-5}
Sulfuric	H_2SO_4	K_1 very large
	HSO_4^-	$K_2 \ 1.2 \times 10^{-2}$
Sulfurous	H_2SO_3	$K_1 \ 1.5 \times 10^{-2}$
	HSO_3^-	$K_2 \ 6.2 \times 10^{-8}$
Hydrated zinc ion	$Zn(H_2O)_n^{+2}$	3×10^{-10}

Base		K_b
Ammonia	NH_3	1.8×10^{-5}
Aniline	$C_6H_5NH_2$	4.0×10^{-10}
Methylamine	CH_3NH_2	5.0×10^{-4}

3. *Dissociation Constants of Complex Ions*

Complex ion	K_d	Complex ion	K_d
$Ag(NH_3)_2^+$	6.8×10^{-8}	$Cu(CN)_3^{-2}$	1×10^{-35}
$Cd(NH_3)_4^{+2}$	1×10^{-7}	$Fe(CN)_6^{-4}$	1×10^{-35}
$Co(NH_3)_6^{+2}$	1.3×10^{-5}	$Fe(CN)_6^{-3}$	1×10^{-42}
$Co(NH_3)_6^{+3}$	2.2×10^{-34}	$Zn(CN)_4^{-2}$	1×10^{-18}
$Cu(NH_3)_4^{+2}$	2.6×10^{-13}	AlF_6^{-3}	1×10^{-21}
$Zn(NH_3)_4^{+2}$	2.6×10^{-10}	FeF_5^{-2}	4×10^{-16}
$HgBr_4^{-2}$	2.3×10^{-22}	HgI_4^{-2}	5×10^{-31}
$HgCl_4^{-2}$	8.0×10^{-16}	$FeSCN^{+2}$	8×10^{-3}
$Ag(CN)_2^-$	1.7×10^{-19}	$Hg(SCN)_4^{-2}$	1×10^{-21}
$Au(CN)_2^-$	5×10^{-39}	$Ag(S_2O_3)_2^{-3}$	6×10^{-14}
$Cd(CN)_4^{-2}$	1.6×10^{-19}		

4. *Solubility Products of Slightly Soluble Strong Electrolytes*

Substance	Formula	K_{sp} (25°C)
Aluminum hydroxide	$Al(OH)_3$	3×10^{-33}
Barium sulfate	$BaSO_4$	1.1×10^{-10}
Cadmium sulfide	CdS	1.0×10^{-28}
Calcium carbonate	$CaCO_3$	7.5×10^{-9}
Calcium fluoride	CaF_2	9.6×10^{-11}
Calcium hydroxide	$Ca(OH)_2$	8×10^{-6}
Calcium oxalate	CaC_2O_4	2.1×10^{-9}
Calcium sulfate	$CaSO_4$	2.4×10^{-5}
Copper (II) sulfide	CuS	8.7×10^{-36}
Copper (I) thiocyanate	$CuCNS$	4×10^{-4}
Iron (III) hydroxide	$Fe(OH)_3$	1.1×10^{-36}
Iron (II) sulfide	FeS	4×10^{-19}
Lead (II) bromide	$PbBr_2$	4.6×10^{-6}
Lead (II) chloride	$PbCl_2$	1.6×10^{-5}
Lead (II) chromate	$PbCrO_4$	2×10^{-15}
Lead (II) phosphate	$Pb_3(PO_4)_2$	3×10^{-44}
Lead (II) sulfate	$PbSO_4$	1.4×10^{-8}
Lead (II) sulfide	PbS	8.4×10^{-28}
Magnesium hydroxide	$Mg(OH)_2$	1.2×10^{-11}
Manganese (II) sulfide	MnS	7×10^{-16}
Mercury (II) sulfide	HgS	1.6×10^{-54}
Silver bromide	$AgBr$	4.8×10^{-13}
Silver chloride	$AgCl$	1.2×10^{-10}
Silver chromate	Ag_2CrO_4	1×10^{-12}
Silver iodide	AgL	1×10^{-16}
Silver phosphate	Ag_3PO_4	1.0×10^{-18}
Silver sulfate	Ag_2SO_4	1.7×10^{-5}
Silver sulfide	Ag_2S	6.8×10^{-5}
Tin (II) sulfide	SnS	1×10^{-26}
Zinc sulfide	ZnS	1.1×10^{-21}

5. *Oxidation–Reduction Potentials**

Half reaction		E	Half reaction		E
Li	— Li$^+$	+3.045	As	— HAsO$_2$ (H$^+$)	−0.2475
K	— K$^+$	+2.925	Bi	— BiO$^+$ (H$^+$)	−0.32
Cs	— Cs$^+$	+2.92	Cu	— Cu^{++}	−0.337
Ba	— Ba^{++}	+2.90	H$_2$O	— O$_2$ (OH$^-$)	−0.401
Sr	— Sr^{++}	+2.89	Mn(OH)$_3$	— MnO$_2$ (NH$_4{}^+$)	−0.50
Ca	— Ca^{++}	+2.87	I$^-$	— I$_2$	−0.5355
Na	— Na$^+$	+2.714	MnO$_2$	— MnO$_4{}^-$ (OH$^-$)	−0.60
Mg	— Mg^{++}	+2.37	H$_2$O$_2$	— O$_2$ (H$^+$)	−0.67
Al	— Al^{+++}	+1.66	Fe^{++}	— Fe^{+++}	−0.771
Mn	— Mn^{++}	+1.18	Hg	— Hg$_2{}^{++}$	−0.789
SO$_3{}^{--}$	— SO$_4{}^{--}$(OH$^-$)	+0.93	Ag	— Ag$^+$	−0.7991
H$_2$	— H$_2$O (OH$^-$)	+0.828	H$_2$O	— O$_2$ (10^{-7} M H$^+$)	−0.815
Zn	— Zn^{++}	+0.763	Hg	— Hg^{++}	−0.854
Cr	— Cr^{+++}	+0.74	H$_2$O	— HO$_2{}^-$ (OH$^-$)	−0.88
H$_2$C$_2$O$_4$	— CO$_2$ (H$^+$)	+0.49	Cl$^-$	— ClO$^-$ (OH$^-$)	−0.89
S^{--}	— S (OH$^-$)	+0.48	Hg$_2{}^{++}$	— Hg^{++}	−0.92
Fe	— Fe^{++}	+0.44	NO	— NO$_3{}^-$ (H$^+$)	−0.96
H$_2$	— H$_2$O (10^{-7} M H$^+$)	+0.414	Br$^-$	— Br$_2$	−1.0652
Cr^{++}	— Cr^{+++}	+0.41	H$_2$O	— O$_2$ (H$^+$)	−1.229
Cd	— Cd^{++}	+0.403	Mn^{++}	— MnO$_2$ (H$^+$)	−1.23
Pb	— PbSO$_4$	+0.356	Cr^{+++}	— Cr$_2$O$_7{}^{--}$ (H$^+$)	−1.33
Co	— Co^{++}	+0.277	Cl$^-$	— Cl$_2$	−1.3595
Ni	— Ni^{++}	+0.250	Pb	— PbO$_2$ (H$^+$)	−1.455
Sn	— Sn^{++}	+0.136	Cl$_2$	— ClO$_3{}^-$ (H$^+$)	−1.47
Cr (OH)$_3$	— CrO$_4{}^{--}$(OH$^-$)	+0.13	Cl$^-$	— HClO (H$^+$)	−1.49
Pb	— Pb^{++}	+0.126	Au	— Au^{+++}	−1.50
HO$_2{}^-$	— O$_2$ (OH$^-$)	+0.076	Mn^{++}	— MnO$_4{}^-$ (H$^+$)	−1.51
H$_2$	— H$^+$	0.000	BiO$^+$	— Bi$_2$O$_4$ (H$^+$)	−1.6
H$_2$S	— S (H$^+$)	−0.141	PbSO$_4$	— PbO$_2$ (H$^+$)	−1.685
Sn^{++}	— Sn^{++++}	−0.15	MnO$_2$	— MnO$_4{}^-$ (H$^+$)	−1.695
H$_2$SO$_3$	— SO$_4{}^{--}$ (H$^+$)	−0.17	H$_2$O	— H$_2$O$_2$ (H$^+$)	−1.77
Sb	— SbO$^+$ (H$^+$)	−0.212	F$^-$	— F$_2$	−2.87
Ag	— AgCl	−0.2222	HF	— F$_2$ (H$^+$)	−3.06

* Values given in Latimer, *Oxidation Potentials*, Second Ed., Prentice-Hall, 1952.

APPENDIX III

1. Logarithms
2. Anti-Logarithms
3. Answers to Even-Numbered Problems

1. *Four Place Logarithms*

N	0	1	2	3	4	5	6	7	8	9	Proportional Parts								
											1	2	3	4	5	6	7	8	9
10	0000	0043	0086	0128	0170	0212	0253	0294	0334	0374	4	8	12	17	21	25	29	33	37
11	0414	0453	0492	0531	0569	0607	0645	0682	0719	0755	4	8	11	15	19	23	26	30	34
12	0792	0828	0864	0899	0934	0969	1004	1038	1072	1106	3	7	10	14	17	21	24	28	31
13	1139	1173	1206	1239	1271	1303	1335	1367	1399	1430	3	6	10	13	16	19	23	26	29
14	1461	1492	1523	1553	1584	1614	1644	1673	1703	1732	3	6	9	12	15	18	21	24	27
15	1761	1790	1818	1847	1875	1903	1931	1959	1987	2014	3	6	8	11	14	17	20	22	25
16	2041	2068	2095	2122	2148	2175	2201	2227	2253	2279	3	5	8	11	13	16	18	21	24
17	2304	2330	2355	2380	2405	2430	2455	2480	2504	2529	2	5	7	10	12	15	17	20	22
18	2553	2577	2601	2625	2648	2672	2695	2718	2742	2765	2	5	7	9	12	14	16	19	21
19	2788	2810	2833	2856	2878	2900	2923	2945	2967	2989	2	4	7	9	11	13	16	18	20
20	3010	3032	3054	3075	3096	3118	3139	3160	3181	3201	2	4	6	8	11	13	15	17	19
21	3222	3243	3263	3284	3304	3324	3345	3365	3385	3404	2	4	6	8	10	12	14	16	18
22	3424	3444	3464	3483	3502	3522	3541	3560	3579	3598	2	4	6	8	10	12	14	15	17
23	3617	3636	3655	3674	3692	3711	3729	3747	3766	3784	2	4	6	7	9	11	13	15	17
24	3802	3820	3838	3856	3874	3892	3909	3927	3945	3962	2	4	5	7	9	11	12	14	16
25	3979	3997	4014	4031	4048	4065	4082	4099	4116	4133	2	3	5	7	9	10	12	14	15
26	4150	4166	4183	4200	4216	4232	4249	4265	4281	4298	2	3	5	7	8	10	11	13	15
27	4314	4330	4346	4362	4378	4393	4409	4425	4440	4456	2	3	5	6	8	9	11	13	14
28	4472	4487	4502	4518	4533	4548	4564	4579	4594	4609	2	3	5	6	8	9	11	12	14
29	4624	4639	4654	4669	4683	4698	4713	4728	4742	4757	1	3	4	6	7	9	10	12	13
30	4771	4786	4800	4814	4829	4843	4857	4871	4886	4900	1	3	4	6	7	9	10	11	13
31	4914	4928	4942	4955	4969	4983	4997	5011	5024	5038	1	3	4	6	7	8	10	11	12
32	5051	5065	5079	5092	5105	5119	5132	5145	5159	5172	1	3	4	5	7	8	9	11	12
33	5185	5198	5211	5224	5237	5250	5263	5276	5289	5302	1	3	4	5	6	8	9	10	12
34	5315	5328	5340	5353	5366	5378	5391	5403	5416	5428	1	3	4	5	6	8	9	10	11
35	5441	5453	5465	5478	5490	5502	5514	5527	5539	5551	1	2	4	5	6	7	9	10	11
36	5563	5575	5587	5599	5611	5623	5635	5647	5658	5670	1	2	4	5	6	7	8	10	11
37	5682	5694	5705	5717	5729	5740	5752	5763	5775	5786	1	2	3	5	6	7	8	9	10
38	5798	5809	5821	5832	5843	5855	5866	5877	5888	5899	1	2	3	5	6	7	8	9	10
39	5911	5922	5933	5944	5955	5966	5977	5988	5999	6010	1	2	3	4	5	7	8	9	10
40	6021	6031	6042	6053	6064	6075	6085	6096	6107	6117	1	2	3	4	5	6	8	9	10
41	6128	6138	6149	6160	6170	6180	6191	6201	6212	6222	1	2	3	4	5	6	7	8	9
42	6232	6243	6253	6263	6274	6284	6294	6304	6314	6325	1	2	3	4	5	6	7	8	9
43	6335	6345	6355	6365	6375	6385	6395	6405	6415	6425	1	2	3	4	5	6	7	8	9
44	6435	6444	6454	6464	6474	6484	6493	6503	6513	6522	1	2	3	4	5	6	7	8	9
45	6532	6542	6551	6561	6571	6580	6590	6599	6609	6618	1	2	3	4	5	6	7	8	9
46	6628	6637	6646	6656	6665	6675	6684	6693	6702	6712	1	2	3	4	5	6	7	7	8
47	6721	6730	6739	6749	6758	6767	6776	6785	6794	6803	1	2	3	4	5	5	6	7	8
48	6812	6821	6830	6839	6848	6857	6866	6875	6884	6893	1	2	3	4	4	5	6	7	8
49	6902	6911	6920	6928	6937	6946	6955	6964	6972	6981	1	2	3	4	4	5	6	7	8
50	6990	6998	7007	7016	7024	7033	7042	7050	7059	7067	1	2	3	3	4	5	6	7	8
51	7076	7084	7093	7101	7110	7118	7126	7135	7143	7152	1	2	3	3	4	5	6	7	8
52	7160	7168	7177	7185	7193	7202	7210	7218	7226	7235	1	2	2	3	4	5	6	7	7
53	7243	7251	7259	7267	7275	7284	7292	7300	7308	7316	1	2	2	3	4	5	6	6	7
54	7324	7332	7340	7348	7356	7364	7372	7380	7388	7396	1	2	2	3	4	5	6	6	7
N	0	1	2	3	4	5	6	7	8	9	1	2	3	4	5	6	7	8	9

1. *Four Place Logarithms*

N	0	1	2	3	4	5	6	7	8	9	Proportional Parts								
											1	2	3	4	5	6	7	8	9
55	7404	7412	7419	7427	7435	7443	7451	7459	7466	7474	1	2	2	3	4	5	5	6	7
56	7482	7490	7497	7505	7513	7520	7528	7536	7543	7551	1	2	2	3	4	5	5	6	7
57	7559	7566	7574	7582	7589	7597	7604	7612	7619	7627	1	2	2	3	4	5	5	6	7
58	7634	7642	7649	7657	7664	7672	7679	7686	7694	7701	1	1	2	3	4	4	5	6	7
59	7709	7716	7723	7731	7738	7745	7752	7760	7767	7774	1	1	2	3	4	4	5	6	7
60	7782	7789	7796	7803	7810	7818	7825	7832	7839	7846	1	1	2	3	4	4	5	6	6
61	7853	7860	7868	7875	7882	7889	7896	7903	7910	7917	1	1	2	3	4	4	5	6	6
62	7924	7931	7938	7945	7952	7959	7966	7973	7980	7987	1	1	2	3	3	4	5	6	6
63	7993	8000	8007	8014	8021	8028	8035	8041	8048	8055	1	1	2	3	3	4	5	5	6
64	8062	8069	8075	8082	8089	8096	8102	8109	8116	8122	1	1	2	3	3	4	5	5	6
65	8129	8136	8142	8149	8156	8162	8169	8176	8182	8189	1	1	2	3	3	4	5	5	6
66	8195	8202	8209	8215	8222	8228	8235	8241	8248	8254	1	1	2	3	3	4	5	5	6
67	8261	8267	8274	8280	8287	8293	8299	8306	8312	8319	1	1	2	3	3	4	5	5	6
68	8325	8331	8338	8344	8351	8357	8363	8370	8376	8382	1	1	2	3	3	4	4	5	6
69	8388	8395	8401	8407	8414	8420	8426	8432	8439	8445	1	1	2	2	3	4	4	5	6
70	8451	8457	8463	8470	8476	8482	8488	8494	8500	8506	1	1	2	2	3	4	4	5	6
71	8513	8519	8525	8531	8537	8543	8549	8555	8561	8567	1	1	2	2	3	4	4	5	5
72	8573	8579	8585	8591	8597	8603	8609	8615	8621	8627	1	1	2	2	3	4	4	5	5
73	8633	8639	8645	8651	8657	8663	8669	8675	8681	8686	1	1	2	2	3	4	4	5	5
74	8692	8698	8704	8710	8716	8722	8727	8733	8739	8745	1	1	2	2	3	4	4	5	5
75	8751	8756	8762	8768	8774	8779	8785	8791	8797	8802	1	1	2	2	3	3	4	5	5
76	8808	8814	8820	8825	8831	8837	8842	8848	8854	8859	1	1	2	2	3	3	4	5	5
77	8865	8871	8876	8882	8887	8893	8899	8904	8910	8915	1	1	2	2	3	3	4	4	5
78	8921	8927	8932	8938	8943	8949	8954	8960	8965	8971	1	1	2	2	3	3	4	4	5
79	8976	8982	8987	8993	8998	9004	9009	9015	9020	9025	1	1	2	2	3	3	4	4	5
80	9031	9036	9042	9047	9053	9058	9063	9069	9074	9079	1	1	2	2	3	3	4	4	5
81	9085	9090	9096	9101	9106	9112	9117	9122	9128	9133	1	1	2	2	3	3	4	4	5
82	9138	9143	9149	9154	9159	9165	9170	9175	9180	9186	1	1	2	2	3	3	4	4	5
83	9191	9196	9201	9206	9212	9217	9222	9227	9232	9238	1	1	2	2	3	3	4	4	5
84	9243	9248	9253	9258	9263	9269	9274	9279	9284	9289	1	1	2	2	3	3	4	4	5
85	9294	9299	9304	9309	9315	9320	9325	9330	9335	9340	1	1	2	2	3	3	4	4	5
86	9345	9350	9355	9360	9365	9370	9375	9380	9385	9390	1	1	2	2	3	3	4	4	5
87	9395	9400	9405	9410	9415	9420	9425	9430	9435	9440	0	1	1	2	2	3	3	4	4
88	9445	9450	9455	9460	9465	9469	9474	9479	9484	9489	0	1	1	2	2	3	3	4	4
89	9494	9499	9504	9509	9513	9518	9523	9528	9533	9538	0	1	1	2	2	3	3	4	4
90	9542	9547	9552	9557	9562	9566	9571	9576	9581	9586	0	1	1	2	2	3	3	4	4
91	9590	9595	9600	9605	9609	9614	9619	9624	9628	9633	0	1	1	2	2	3	3	4	4
92	9638	9643	9647	9652	9657	9661	9666	9671	9675	9680	0	1	1	2	2	3	3	4	4
93	9685	9689	9694	9699	9703	9708	9713	9717	9722	9727	0	1	1	2	2	3	3	4	4
94	9731	9736	9741	9745	9750	9754	9759	9763	9768	9773	0	1	1	2	2	3	3	4	4
95	9777	9782	9786	9791	9795	9800	9805	9809	9814	9818	0	1	1	2	2	3	3	4	4
96	9823	9827	9832	9836	9841	9845	9850	9854	9859	9863	0	1	1	2	2	3	3	4	4
97	9868	9872	9877	9881	9886	9890	9894	9899	9903	9908	0	1	1	2	2	3	3	4	4
98	9912	9917	9921	9926	9930	9934	9939	9943	9948	9952	0	1	1	2	2	3	3	4	4
99	9956	9961	9965	9969	9974	9978	9983	9987	9991	9996	0	1	1	2	2	3	3	3	4
N	0	1	2	3	4	5	6	7	8	9	1	2	3	4	5	6	7	8	9

2. Antilogarithms

	0	1	2	3	4	5	6	7	8	9	Proportional Parts								
											1	2	3	4	5	6	7	8	9
.00	1000	1002	1005	1007	1009	1012	1014	101ȏ	1019	1021	0	0	1	1	1	1	2	2	2
.01	1023	1026	1028	1030	1033	1035	1038	1040	1042	1045	0	0	1	1	1	1	2	2	2
.02	1047	1050	1052	1054	1057	1059	1062	1064	1067	1069	0	0	1	1	1	1	2	2	2
.03	1072	1074	1076	1079	1081	1084	1086	1089	1091	1094	0	0	1	1	1	1	2	2	2
.04	1096	1099	1102	1104	1107	1109	1112	1114	1117	1119	0	1	1	1	1	2	2	2	2
.05	1122	1125	1127	1130	1132	1135	1138	1140	1143	1146	0	1	1	1	1	2	2	2	2
.06	1148	1151	1153	1156	1159	1161	1164	1167	1169	1172	0	1	1	1	1	2	2	2	2
.07	1175	1178	1180	1183	1186	1189	1191	1194	1197	1199	0	1	1	1	1	2	2	2	2
.08	1202	1205	1208	1211	1213	1216	1219	1222	1225	1227	0	1	1	1	1	2	2	2	3
.09	1230	1233	1236	1239	1242	1245	1247	1250	1253	1256	0	1	1	1	1	2	2	2	3
.10	1259	1262	1265	1268	1271	1274	1276	1279	1282	1285	0	1	1	1	1	2	2	2	3
.11	1288	1291	1294	1297	1300	1303	1306	1309	1312	1315	0	1	1	1	2	2	2	2	3
.12	1318	1321	1324	1327	1330	1334	1337	1340	1343	1346	0	1	1	1	2	2	2	3	3
.13	1349	1352	1355	1358	1361	1365	1368	1371	1374	1377	0	1	1	1	2	2	2	3	3
.14	1380	1384	1387	1390	1393	1396	1400	1403	1406	1409	0	1	1	1	2	2	2	3	3
.15	1413	1416	1419	1422	1426	1429	1432	1435	1439	1442	0	1	1	1	2	2	2	3	3
.16	1445	1449	1452	1455	1459	1462	1466	1469	1472	1476	0	1	1	1	2	2	2	3	3
.17	1479	1483	1486	1489	1493	1496	1500	1503	1507	1510	0	1	1	1	2	2	2	3	3
.18	1514	1517	1521	1524	1528	1531	1535	1538	1542	1545	0	1	1	1	2	2	2	3	3
.19	1549	1552	1556	1560	1563	1567	1570	1574	1578	1581	0	1	1	1	2	2	3	3	3
.20	1585	1589	1592	1596	1600	1603	1607	1611	1614	1618	0	1	1	1	2	2	3	3	3
.21	1622	1626	1629	1633	1637	1641	1644	1648	1652	1656	0	1	1	2	2	2	3	3	3
.22	1660	1663	1667	1671	1675	1679	1683	1687	1690	1694	0	1	1	2	2	2	3	3	3
.23	1698	1702	1706	1710	1714	1718	1722	1726	1730	1734	0	1	1	2	2	2	3	3	4
.24	1738	1742	1746	1750	1754	1758	1762	1766	1770	1774	0	1	1	2	2	2	3	3	4
.25	1778	1782	1786	1791	1795	1799	1803	1807	1811	1816	0	1	1	2	2	2	3	3	4
.26	1820	1824	1828	1832	1837	1841	1845	1849	1854	1858	0	1	1	2	2	3	3	3	4
.27	1862	1866	1871	1875	1879	1884	1888	1892	1897	1901	0	1	1	2	2	3	3	3	4
.28	1905	1910	1914	1919	1923	1928	1932	1936	1941	1945	0	1	1	2	2	3	3	4	4
.29	1950	1954	1959	1963	1968	1972	1977	1982	1986	1991	0	1	1	2	2	3	3	4	4
.30	1995	2000	2004	2009	2014	2018	2023	2028	2032	2037	0	1	1	2	2	3	3	4	4
.31	2042	2046	2051	2056	2061	2065	2070	2075	2080	2084	0	1	1	2	2	3	3	4	4
.32	2089	2094	2099	2104	2109	2113	2118	2123	2128	2133	0	1	1	2	2	3	3	4	4
.33	2138	2143	2148	2153	2158	2163	2168	2173	2178	2183	0	1	1	2	2	3	3	4	4
.34	2188	2193	2198	2203	2208	2213	2218	2223	2228	2234	1	1	2	2	3	3	4	4	5
.35	2239	2244	2249	2254	2259	2265	2270	2275	2280	2286	1	1	2	2	3	3	4	4	5
.36	2291	2296	2301	2307	2312	2317	2323	2328	2333	2339	1	1	2	2	3	3	4	4	5
.37	2344	2350	2355	2360	2366	2371	2377	2382	2388	2393	1	1	2	2	3	3	4	4	5
.38	2399	2404	2410	2415	2421	2427	2432	2438	2443	2449	1	1	2	2	3	3	4	4	5
.39	2455	2460	2466	2472	2477	2483	2489	2495	2500	2506	1	1	2	2	3	3	4	5	5
.40	2512	2518	2523	2529	2535	2541	2547	2553	2559	2564	1	1	2	2	3	4	4	5	5
.41	2570	2576	2582	2588	2594	2600	2606	2612	2618	2624	1	1	2	2	3	4	4	5	5
.42	2630	2636	2642	2649	2655	2661	2667	2673	2679	2685	1	1	2	2	3	4	4	5	6
.43	2692	2698	2704	2710	2716	2723	2729	2735	2742	2748	1	1	2	3	3	4	4	5	6
.44	2754	2761	2767	2773	2780	2786	2793	2799	2805	2812	1	1	2	3	3	4	4	5	6
.45	2818	2825	2831	2838	2844	2851	2858	2864	2871	2877	1	1	2	3	3	4	5	5	6
.46	2884	2891	2897	2904	2911	2917	2924	2931	2938	2944	1	1	2	3	3	4	5	5	6
.47	2951	2958	2965	2972	2979	2985	2992	2999	3006	3013	1	1	2	3	3	4	5	5	6
.48	3020	3027	3034	3041	3048	3055	3062	3069	3076	3083	1	1	2	3	4	4	5	6	6
.49	3090	3097	3105	3112	3119	3126	3133	3141	3148	3155	1	1	2	3	4	4	5	6	6
	0	1	2	3	4	5	6	7	8	9	1	2	3	4	5	6	7	8	9

2. *Antilogarithms*

	0	1	2	3	4	5	6	7	8	9	Proportional Parts								
											1	2	3	4	5	6	7	8	9
.50	3162	3170	3177	3184	3192	3199	3206	3214	3221	3228	1	1	2	3	4	4	5	6	7
.51	3236	3243	3251	3258	3266	3273	3281	3289	3296	3304	1	2	2	3	4	5	5	6	7
.52	3311	3319	3327	3334	3342	3350	3357	3365	3373	3381	1	2	2	3	4	5	5	6	7
.53	3388	3396	3404	3412	3420	3428	3436	3443	3451	3459	1	2	2	3	4	5	6	6	7
.54	3467	3475	3483	3491	3499	3508	3516	3524	3532	3540	1	2	2	3	4	5	6	6	7
.55	3548	3556	3565	3573	3581	3589	3597	3606	3614	3622	1	2	2	3	4	5	6	7	7
.56	3631	3639	3648	3656	3664	3673	3681	3690	3698	3707	1	2	3	3	4	5	6	7	8
.57	3715	3724	3733	3741	3750	3758	3767	3776	3784	3793	1	2	3	3	4	5	6	7	8
.58	3802	3811	3819	3828	3837	3846	3855	3864	3873	3882	1	2	3	4	4	5	6	7	8
.59	3890	3899	3908	3917	3926	3936	3945	3954	3963	3972	1	2	3	4	5	5	6	7	8
.60	3981	3990	3999	4009	4018	4027	4036	4046	4055	4064	1	2	3	4	5	6	6	7	8
.61	4074	4083	4093	4102	4111	4121	4130	4140	4150	4159	1	2	3	4	5	6	7	8	9
.62	4169	4178	4188	4198	4207	4217	4227	4236	4246	4256	1	2	3	4	5	6	7	8	9
.63	4266	4276	4285	4295	4305	4315	4325	4335	4345	4355	1	2	3	4	5	6	7	8	9
.64	4365	4375	4385	4395	4406	4416	4426	4436	4446	4457	1	2	3	4	5	6	7	8	9
.65	4467	4477	4487	4498	4508	4519	4529	4539	4550	4560	1	2	3	4	5	6	7	8	9
.66	4571	4581	4592	4603	4613	4624	4634	4645	4656	4667	1	2	3	4	5	6	7	9	10
.67	4677	4688	4699	4710	4721	4732	4742	4753	4764	4775	1	2	3	4	5	7	8	9	10
.68	4786	4797	4808	4819	4831	4842	4853	4864	4875	4887	1	2	3	4	6	7	8	9	10
.69	4898	4909	4920	4932	4943	4955	4966	4977	4989	5000	1	2	3	5	6	7	8	9	10
.70	5012	5023	5035	5047	5058	5070	5082	5093	5105	5117	1	2	4	5	6	7	8	9	11
.71	5129	5140	5152	5164	5176	5188	5200	5212	5224	5236	1	2	4	5	6	7	8	10	11
.72	5248	5260	5272	5284	5297	5309	5321	5333	5346	5358	1	2	4	5	6	7	9	10	11
.73	5370	5383	5395	5408	5420	5433	5445	5458	5470	5483	1	3	4	5	6	8	9	10	11
.74	5495	5508	5521	5534	5546	5559	5572	5585	5598	5610	1	3	4	5	6	8	9	10	12
.75	5623	5636	5649	5662	5675	5689	5702	5715	5728	5741	1	3	4	5	7	8	9	10	12
.76	5754	5768	5781	5794	5808	5821	5834	5848	5861	5875	1	3	4	5	7	8	9	11	12
.77	5888	5902	5916	5929	5943	5957	5970	5984	5998	6012	1	3	4	5	7	8	10	11	12
.78	6026	6039	6053	6067	6081	6095	6109	6124	6138	6152	1	3	4	6	7	8	10	11	13
.79	6166	6180	6194	6209	6223	6237	6252	6266	6281	6295	1	3	4	6	7	9	10	11	13
.80	6310	6324	6339	6353	6368	6383	6397	6412	6427	6442	1	3	4	6	7	9	10	12	13
.81	6457	6471	6486	6501	6516	6531	6546	6561	6577	6592	2	3	5	6	8	9	11	12	14
.82	6607	6622	6637	6653	6668	6683	6699	6714	6730	6745	2	3	5	6	8	9	11	12	14
.83	6761	6776	6792	6808	6823	6839	6855	6871	6887	6902	2	3	5	6	8	9	11	13	14
.84	6918	6934	6950	6966	6982	6998	7015	7031	7047	7063	2	3	5	6	8	10	11	13	15
.85	7079	7096	7112	7129	7145	7161	7178	7194	7211	7228	2	3	5	7	8	10	12	13	15
.86	7244	7261	7278	7295	7311	7328	7345	7362	7379	7396	2	3	5	7	8	10	12	13	15
.87	7413	7430	7447	7464	7482	7499	7516	7534	7551	7568	2	3	5	7	9	10	12	14	16
.88	7586	7603	7621	7638	7656	7674	7691	7709	7727	7745	2	4	5	7	9	11	12	14	16
.89	7762	7780	7798	7816	7834	7852	7870	7889	7907	7925	2	4	5	7	9	11	13	14	16
.90	7943	7962	7980	7998	8017	8035	8054	8072	8091	8110	2	4	6	7	9	11	13	15	17
.91	8128	8147	8166	8185	8204	8222	8241	8260	8279	8299	2	4	6	8	9	11	13	15	17
.92	8318	8337	8356	8375	8395	8414	8433	8453	8472	8492	2	4	6	8	10	12	14	15	17
.93	8511	8531	8551	8570	8590	8610	8630	8650	8670	8690	2	4	6	8	10	12	14	16	18
.94	8710	8730	8750	8770	8790	8810	8831	8851	8872	8892	2	4	6	8	10	12	14	16	18
.95	8913	8933	8954	8974	8995	9016	9036	9057	9078	9099	2	4	6	8	10	12	15	17	19
.96	9120	9141	9162	9183	9204	9226	9247	9268	9290	9311	2	4	6	8	11	13	15	17	19
.97	9333	9354	9376	9397	9419	9441	9462	9484	9506	9528	2	4	7	9	11	13	15	17	20
.98	9550	9572	9594	9616	9638	9661	9683	9705	9727	9750	2	4	7	9	11	13	16	18	20
.99	9772	9795	9817	9840	9863	9886	9908	9931	9954	9977	2	5	7	9	11	14	16	18	20
	0	1	2	3	4	5	6	7	8	9	1	2	3	4	5	6	7	8	9

Answers to Even-Numbered Problems

Section 1.4

2. Commutative law of addition
4. Associative law of addition
6. Distributive law
8. Associative law of multiplication
10. Distributive law
12. Associative law of addition
14. Associative law of multiplication
16. Associative law of addition
18. Commutative law of addition
20. Distributive law
22. Commutative law of multiplication
24. Associative law of multiplication.

Section 1.5

2. Commutative law of multiplication
4. Commutative law of multiplication
6. Distributive law
8. Commutative law of multiplication
10. Commutative law of multiplication
12. Commutative law of multiplication
14. Distributive law
16. Commutative law of multiplication.

Section 2.6

2. 1	14. 5	24. -56	34. -2
4. 3	16. 1	26. 60	36. 6
6. 5	18. -16	28. 24	38. 4
8. -14	20. 28	30. 90	40. -2
10. -8	22. 47	32. 252	42. $-\frac{7}{3}$.
12. 3			

Section 2.7

2. 241°K
4. -73°C
6. 0°C
8. 0°C
10. 66°C
12. -73°C

14. 1.73
16. 1.36
18. 0.41
20. $Cl_2 + 2 Br^- \rightarrow 2 Cl^- + Br_2$, 0.294 V, yes
22. $2 Li + Co^{++} \rightarrow 2 Li^+ + Co$, 2.77 V, yes.

Section 3.3

2. $\frac{1}{2}$	12. $\frac{23}{24}$	20. $\frac{5}{32}$ (d)
4. 3	14. $\frac{41}{8}$	22. $\frac{144}{187}$ (d)
6. $\frac{7}{17}$	16. 4 (d, a)	24. $\frac{13}{75}$ (b, d, a)
8. $\frac{2}{9}$	18. $\frac{12}{13}$ (d, a)	26. $\frac{121}{36}$ (b).
10. $\frac{23}{24}$		

Section 3.4

2. $195x/308$

4. $-m - n/12$

6. $29x + \frac{2}{21}$

8. a/bc

10. xw/yf

12. $a/b.$

Section 3.5

2. 138 mm

4. 1000 l

6. 5900 A

8. 14.7 cc

10. 0.38 moles

12. 1.11 moles

14. 3.301 M

16. 0.56 l

18. 15 030 kcal.

Section 4.5

2. 7.2×10^6

4. 4.51×10^{-1}

6. 6×10^{-5}

8. 5×10^{-7}

10. $2\,000\,000$

12. 0.056

14. 0.0000035

16. 0.007

18. $125\,000$

20. 4×10^4

22. 1×10^7

24. 0.72

26. 4×10^7

28. 2×10^4

30. x^5

32. x^{14}

34. $b^8.$

Section 4.6

2. 1×10^3 liters

4. 20 kg

6. 4×10^{-8} cm, 4×10^{-10} m

8. 3×10^{-2} cm

10. 6.02×10^{23}

12. 6.02

14. 141.6 gm

16. 1×10^{-8}

18. 2.0×10^{-5}

20. $8.0 \times 10^{-6}.$

Section 5.3

2. 2, 2, 2, 2, 3

4. 2, 2, 2, 5, 5

6. 5, 73

8. 2, 2, 71

10. $4(2a - 3)$

12. $x(3 - 4)$

14. $mo(n - 1)$

16. $3x(7y - 1)$

18. $(a^2 - 7)(a^2 - 3a + 5)$

20. $(a - b)(x^2 + y^2 - 3)$

22. $(x - 2)(3h - 4k)$

24. $(m + n)(m - n)$

26. $2(3y - 2x)(3y + 2x)$

28. $(7a + 1)(7a - 1)$

30. $b(y + x)(y - x)$

32. $2z(x - y)(x + y)$

34. $(10b - b^2)(10b + b^2)$

36. $(m + n + c)(m + n - c)$

38. $(2x + y - 5z)(2x + y + 5z)$

40. $(m + n - o + p)(m + n + o - p)$

42. $3(m - n + 3)(m - n - 3)$

44. $(m - n)(m^2 + mn + n^2)$

46. $(a - 5)(a^2 + 5a + 25)$

48. $m^3[(m - n)^3 + 1]$

50. $10ab + 8ax$

52. $-15zx - 10zy$

54. $2a^3 + 4a$

56. $x^2 + x - 12$

58. $6a^2 + 5a - 6$

60. $x^3 - 6x^2 - 5x - 12$

62. $m^2 - n^2$

64. $m^2x^{2a} - n^2$

66. $9x^4 + 3x^3 - 6x^2 + 6x^3y + 2x^2y$
    $-4xy - 3x^2y^2 - xy^2 + 2y^2.$

Section 5.4

2. -35.5
4. 30
6. 1.06

8. 29.5^0
10. 0.63 gm Ca, 0.37 gm Zn.

Section 6.5

8. conditional
10. neither
12. conditional
14. $\frac{13}{8}$

16. $-\frac{1}{4}$
18. $\frac{6}{5}$
20. 2
22. $R = -Ar/(2 - A)$

24. $m_1 = fr^2/Gm_2$
26. $w = P - 2L/2$
28. $r_2 = qr_1/(q - t_0Vr_1)$
30. $T_2 = T_1(1 - E)$.

Section 6.6

2. $°K = °C + 273$
4. mol wt. = gm of SO_2/moles of SO_2
6. $V = nRT/P$
8. $T_2 = P_2V_2T_1/P_1V_1$
10. $M_{H_2} = M_{CO_2}r^2_{CO_2}/r^2_{H_2}$

12. $m = \dfrac{\text{lowering of freezing point}}{K_f}$

14. $P_{CO} = \sqrt{K_pP_{CO_2}}$

16. $[CN^-] = 4\sqrt{\dfrac{K_d[Cd(CN)_4{}^{--}]}{[Cd^{++}]}}$

18. $[IO_3^-] = \sqrt{\dfrac{K_{sp}}{[Pb^{++}]}}$.

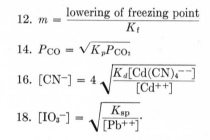

Section 7.5

14. -1
16. 1/3
18. 2/3
20. 1/2

22. $-1/4$
24. 1
26. 2/3.

Section 8.6

2. $x = -2, y = 3$
4. $x = \frac{2}{3}, y = -\frac{1}{3}$
6. $x = \frac{1}{2}, y = -\frac{1}{2}$
8. $x = 5\frac{8}{13}, y = -3\frac{1}{3}$
10. $x = 2, y = -\frac{3}{2}$
12. $x = 3, y = 0$
14. dependent, $x = 0, y = 0$
16. consistent and independent,
    $x = -1, y = 1$

18. dependent, $x = 0, y = 0$
20. inconsistent, no solution
22. $x = \frac{3}{4}, y = 4$
24. $x = 2, y = 40$
26. $x = 2\frac{1}{3}, y = 1\frac{2}{7}, z = 1\frac{5}{7}$
28. $x = -4, y = -8, z = -1$.

Section 8.7

2. 2.67 l 95%, 7.33 l 20%
4. 83.33 gm 5%, 166.67 gm 8%
6. 1.62 gm
8. 71.6°F, 295°K

10. 65.5
12. 1.04 gm NaBr, 0.28 gm NaI
14. 0.186 gm CO_2, 2.546 gm SO_3
16. 0.83 l 0.4N HCl, 1.67 l 0.1 N HCl.

Section 9.5

2. $2\sqrt{6}$

4. $6\sqrt{2}$

6. $\sqrt{2}/3$

8. $\sqrt{6}/9$

10. $\sqrt{21}/6$

12. $\sqrt{15}/6$

14. $\dfrac{2 + \sqrt{3}}{2}$

16. $2 + \sqrt{7}$

18. $\dfrac{-2 + \sqrt{6}}{3}$.

Section 9.6

2. $1/\sqrt{14}$

4. $AgCl$: 1.31×10^{-5} M, $CaCO_3$: 6.86×10^{-5} M

6. 10^{-7} M

8. $\sqrt{8.9} \times 10^{-5}$ M

10. 3.16×10^{-2} M.

Section 10.3

2. $x = \dfrac{-B \pm \sqrt{B^2 + 4A/C}}{2A}$

4. $3, -2$

6. $\dfrac{3a}{4}, \dfrac{-a}{3}$

8. $\dfrac{-1 \pm \sqrt{265}}{6}$

10. $\dfrac{r \pm \sqrt{r^2 - 0.8}}{0.4}$

12. 26 ft

14. 10 or -13.

Section 10.4

2. 1.96×10^{-2} M

4. 3.65×10^{-4} M

6. 3.58×10^{-2} M

8. $2/3$

10. 16.68%

12. $\dfrac{-(a + b)K \pm \sqrt{[K(a + b)]^2 + 4(Kab)(4 - K)}}{2(4 - K)}$.

Section 11.5

2. $y = x^2$

4. $y = (x + z)^2$

6. 3

8. $y = x + 2$

10. $y = x^2$.

Section 11.6

Constant	Variables
2. $1/2$	K.E., m, V
4. k	P, V, T
6. R	n, P, V, T
8. K_{eq}	[HI], [H$_2$], [I$_2$]
10. K_i	[H$^+$], [C$_2$H$_3$O$_2{}^-$], [HC$_2$H$_3$O$_2$]
12. k	[H$_2$], [I$_2$], specific rate
14. R, 2.3, $E_{act.}$	k_1, k_2, T_1, T_2.

Section 12.5

2. $x < 3$

4. $x > -2$

6. $x > 1\frac{5}{7}$

8. $x > 4$

10. $x < 2$

12. $-5 \leqq x \leqq 1$

14. $-3 > x > 2$

16. $-3 < -2 < -1.5 < -1 < 0 < \sqrt{2} < 2 < 3$

18. (a) false, (d) true, (f) false

20. $2 > x > 4$

22. $4 > x > 5$

24. $-6 > x > 2$

26. $1 > x > -2/3$

28. $-5 > x > -1$.

Section 12.6

2. no solid, solid, solid, no solid

4. [Cd^{++}][S^{--}] 1.0×10^{-28}
   [Zn^{++}][S^{--}] 1.1×10^{-21}

6. No.

Section 13.11

2. 5	16. .4082	30. $\bar{1}$.4166	44. $\bar{2}$.5480	58. 316.2
4. -1	18. .6928	32. $\bar{2}$.7267	46. $\bar{1}$.6705	60. 8.207
6. 7	20. .4330	34. $\bar{4}$.6551	48. 1.6663	62. 5.633×10^9
8. 3	22. 2.8621	36. 2.0414	50. 1.6935	64. 1.587×10^7
10. 1	24. $\bar{1}$.8621	38. $\bar{1}$.7566	52. 0.9142	66. 0.005793
12. -4	26. 2.4548	40. 3.7226	54. $\bar{1}$.7508	68. 2.085
14. .9708	28. 1.6839	42. 0.0241	56. 49.36	70. 2.695.

72. 0.1311

74. 0.004201

76. 25.5

78. 159.3

80. 3.4×10^{-7}

82. 0.0407

84. 0.883

86. 0.653.

Section 13.12

2. 11
4. 3.31
6. 9.62
8. 12.89
10. 1×10^{-4}
12. 5.6×10^{-5}

14. 4.0×10^{-14}
16. AgBr: 6.9×10^{-7} M
    $Mg(OH)_2$: 1.4×10^{-4} M
18. $+0.23$ V
20. $+0.30$ V.

Section 14.5

2. 3
4. 6
6. 3
8. 1/2
10. $x = \dfrac{\log 24}{\log 3}$
12. $\dfrac{\log 116}{\log 5}$
14. $\log \left(\tfrac{8.0}{3}\right) + 2$
16. $\log \left(\dfrac{1.26}{1.08}\right)$

18. $\log \left(\dfrac{3}{1.10}\right)$
20. $\dfrac{\log x - \log a}{\log y}$
22. $\dfrac{\log x - \log 3}{\log y}$
24. $\dfrac{\log x - \log 3}{\log x_0}$
26. $\dfrac{\ln n - \ln n_0}{h}$.

Section 14.6

2. $\dfrac{C_0}{C} = 10^{kt/2.303}$
4. $k = \dfrac{2.303}{k(a-b)} \log \dfrac{b}{a} + \dfrac{2.303}{k(a-b)} \log \dfrac{a-x}{b-x}$
6. $\log k = -\dfrac{Ea}{2.303RT} + 5.65$

8. $E = E^0 - 0.0592 \log \dfrac{[\text{Products}]}{[\text{Reactants}]}$
10. 0.969 V.

Section 15.7

2. 2
4. 4
6. 4
8. 2
10. 212
12. 0.62

14. 443.8
16. 0.9
18. 129
20. 0.064
22. 6.07
24. 3.

Section 16.6

2. 18.2
4. $F_1 + F_2 + \cdots = 0$

6. 26 ft lb
8. 45 m/hr

10. 6 $\dot{m}$/hr/min
12. $F = ma$
14. $M = mv$
16. $\Delta M = m(v - u)$
18. $d = m/v$
20. 51.8
22. 4.87
24. 146.2

26. 14.5, 10.5
28. 26, 30
30. $2\frac{11}{12}$
32. 69.3 ml water
34. 17.5 miles
36. 10 and 15
38. 30 mph, 40 mph.

INDEX

(The topics involved in the algebra and chemistry problems are also indexed. Problems related to specific topics are indicated by page and problem number.)

abscissa, 37
acetic acid, ionization of, 62
activity, 102
algebraic notation
  related problems: 114, Nos. 1–16; 115, Nos. 17–36; 116, Nos. 37, 38.
antilogarithm, 89
antilogarithms, table of, 128, 129
arithmetic, universal truth of, 29
Arrhenius equation, 103
  related problems: 44, No. 10; 77, No. 14; 104, Nos. 5–7
associative Law of Addition, 1, 2
associative Law of Multiplication, 1, 2
atomic weights, table of, 118, 119
Avogadro's number
  related problems: 22, Nos. 9–12, 14, 15
axioms, 1
  related problems: 3, Nos. 1–24

binomial, 17
boiling point elevation
  related problem: 77, No. 7
Boyle's law, 2, 75, 111
  related problem: 43, No. 9

calorimetry, 24
characteristic, 86
  related problems: 95, Nos. 1–12
Charles' law, 38, 39, 112
  related problems: 42, Nos. 1, 2; 43, No. 7; 77, No. 3
chemical reaction, mole relationship, 32
chemical reaction, weight and volume relationships, 33

chemicals, mixing of, 53
  related problems: 54, Nos. 1–4
coefficient, 17
common abbreviations, table of, 117
commutative Law of Addition, 1
commutative Law of Multiplication, 1
concentration
  related problem: 27, No. 4
conjugate acid, 64
constant, 70
  related problems: 77, Nos. 1–15
conversion factors, table of, 118
cubic equation, 30

Dalton's Law of Partial Pressures, 2
  related problem: 4, No. 3
decay constant, 102
degree of certainty, 107
density, 13, 74, 111
  related problems: 35, No. 1; 16, No. 9
determinants, 46
diffusion
  related problem: 35, No. 10
dilute solutions, rule for, 62
dilution of solutions
  related problems: 35, No. 11; 55, No. 16
dissociation constant
  related problems: 36, No. 16; 55, No. 13; 60, No. 10; 96, No. 17
dissociation constants, table of, 122
dissociation, degree of, 66
distributive law, 1, 2
double-notation, 47

electrochemistry, 8, 94, 95

137

related problems: 10, Nos. 13–22; 104, Nos. 8–10

elimination method, 46

equation
  conditional, 29
  degree of, 29
  empirical, 41
  first degree, 30, 61
  identical, 29
  linear, 30
  second degree, 30, 61

equilibrium
  related problems: 27, Nos. 6, 7; 69, Nos. 8–13

equilibrium, chemical, 59

equilibrium constant, 34, 65, 66
  related problem: 77, No. 8

equilibrium constant (K_p), 67

equilibrium, gaseous, 25, 34

equivalent equations, 30
  related problems: 35, Nos. 13–30

esterification, 65
  related problem: 69, No. 8

exponent, 17, 87

exponential
  curve, 99
  equation, 100
  notation, 109
  number, 87

exponential functions
  related problems: 103, Nos. 1–27

exponential functions, graph of
  related problems: 104, Nos. 28–36

exponential numbers
  related problems: 21, Nos. 1–35

exponential numbers, rules for, 18

factor, 23

factoring, 23

Faraday's Law of Electrolysis
  related problems: 4, No. 12; 54, No. 10

first-order reaction
  related problems: 104, Nos. 1, 2

freezing point depression, 75
  related problem: 35, No. 12

function, 70, 71
  related problems: 75, Nos. 1–6; 76, Nos. 7–23; 77, Nos. 1–15

functions, graphing of, 72

fundamental principle, 11, 33
  related problems: 15, Nos. 1–26

gas law
  related problem: 43, No. 7

gas laws
  related problems: 4, Nos. 2, 8, 9; 35, Nos. 5, 7, 8; 44, No. 11

gas laws, combined
  related problem: 77, No. 4

gases, diffusion of, 58
  related problems: 59, Nos. 1–3

Gay-Lussac's Law
  related problem: 42, No. 3

gram atoms
  related problem: 35, No. 3

gram equivalent, 14
  related problems: 16, Nos. 16, 17, 19

gram molecular volume, 51
  related problems: 54, Nos. 6, 7

graphs
  related problems: 42, Nos. 1–12

graphs, chemical application
  related problems: 43, Nos. 1–9; 44, Nos. 10, 11

Greek alphabet, 117

half-life, 101, 102

heat, 2, 24
  related problem: 36, No. 19

heat of activation, 103

hydrolysis, 20
  related problems: 60, No. 7; 68, Nos. 5–7

hydrolysis constant, 64

hypotenuse, 56

ideal gas equation, 67
  related problems: 4, Nos. 4, 9, 10; 35, Nos. 6, 9; 43, Nos. 4, 5; 77, No. 5

identities
  related problems: 34, Nos. 1–8; 35, Nos. 9–12

inequalities, 78
  related problems: 84, Nos. 1–28

inequalities, graphical solution
  related problems: 84, Nos. 29–37

inequalities
  linear, 79
  quadratic, 79–82
  rules for, 78

inequality, graph of, 80, 81

interpolation, 88

ionization, 19
  related problems: 60, No. 5; 68, Nos. 1–4, 6

ionization constant, 62, 63, 83
  related problems: 4, No. 16; 22, Nos. 18,
              19; 27, No. 9; 36, Nos.
              15, 17; 60, No. 10; 77,
              No. 10
ionization constants, table of, 121
ion product of water
  related problems: 22, Nos. 16, 17; 60, No. 6
irrational numbers, 56

kinetic energy
  related problem: 77, No. 2
kinetics, 42
  related problems: 104, Nos. 1–4

linear equation, 41, 61
  graph of, 38
  pair of, 45, 52
logarithmic
  curve, 98
  function, 101
  process, 100
logarithms, chemical application
  related problems: 104, Nos. 1–8; 105, Nos.
          9, 10
logarithms
  common, 86
  division of, 91
  multiplication of, 90
  Napierian, 97
  natural, 86, 97
  table of, 126, 127
logarithms, numbers of, 89
  related problems: 96, Nos. 55–66
logarithms, use of
  related problems: 96, Nos. 67–86
logarithms, use with dissociation constants
  related problem: 96, No. 17
logarithms, use in electrochemistry
  related problem: 96, Nos. 18–20
logarithms, use in pH
  related problems: 96, Nos. 1–15
logarithms, use in Nernst equation, 93
logarithms, use in solubility product, 93
  related problem: 96, No. 16
logarithms, use with powers, 92

mantissa, 86, 87
  related problems: 95, Nos. 13–21
measurement, scientific, 106
mixture of gases
  related problem: 55, No. 14

mixture of metals, analysis of, 50
mixture of salts
  related problems: 54, No. 12; 55, Nos. 15,
          17
mixture of salts, analysis of, 51
mixtures, stoichiometry of, 28
molality, 75
  related problem: 16, No. 13
molarity, 14
  related problems: 16, No. 14; 60, No. 10
mole, 13, 65
  related problems: 16, Nos. 10–12; 22, Nos.
          11–13; 35, No. 4; 69,
          Nos. 12, 13
mole relationships, 32
molecules, collision of, 19
monomial, 17
multiplication, algebraic
  related problems: 27, Nos. 50–65

natural logarithms, chemical application
  related problems: 104, Nos. 1, 4, 8
Nernst equation, 93
  related problem: 77, No. 13
nitrogen tetroxide, dissociation of, 66
normality, 14
  related problems: 16, Nos. 15, 16
number, logarithm of, 88
  related problems: 95, Nos. 22–54

ordered pairs, 72
  related problems: 76, Nos. 8–23
ordinate, 37
osmotic pressure
  related problem: 77, No. 6
oxidation number, 7
oxidation-reduction potentials, table of, 124

pairs of equations
  related problems: 53, Nos. 1–12
parabola, 73
partial pressure, 67
pH, 92
  related problems: 4, No. 15; 77, No. 11; 96,
          Nos. 1–15
pH, calculation from $[H^+]$, 92
physical-chemical constants, table of, 117
polynomial, 17, 29
polynomial, factoring of, 23
  related problems: 26, Nos. 10–48
power, 17, 92
precipitation, 58

prime factor
  related problems: 26, Nos. 1–9
prime numbers, 23
problems, rules for solution, 112
proportional parts, 89
proportionality constant, 39

quadratic, 30
quadratic equation, 67
quadratic formula, 61, 66
  related problems: 68, Nos. 1–14
quartic, 30

radioactivity, 100
rectangular coordinates, 37
reductio ad absurdum, 56
roots, 74
rounding numbers, rules for, 109

saturated solution, 82
second-order reaction
  related problem: 104, No. 4
signed numbers, 5, 6, 7
  related problems: 9, Nos. 1–42
significant figures, 63, 107
  related problems: 110, Nos. 1–9
significant figures, addition, 108
  related problems: 110, Nos. 10–12
significant figures, division
  related problems: 110, Nos. 22–25
significant figures, multiplication
  related problems: 110, Nos. 16–21
significant figures, subtraction, 108
  related problems: 110, Nos. 13–15
slope, 38
  related problems: 42, Nos. 13–26
sodium cyanide, hydrolysis of, 64
solubility product, 20, 58, 59, 82, 93
  related problems: 4, No. 17; 22, No. 20; 36,
    No. 18; 54, No. 11; 55,
    No. 13; 60, Nos. 4, 8, 9;
    77, No. 9; 84, Nos. 1, 2;
    85, Nos. 3–6; 96, No. 16
solubility product constants, table of, 123

solutions
  related problems: 4, Nos. 11, 13, 14
specific gravity
  related problems: 27, Nos. 1, 5
specific heat, 2, 40
specific rate
  related problem: 77, No. 12
square root, 57
  related problems: 59, Nos. 1–18
square roots, rules of, 57
substitution method, 45
systems of equations, solution of
  related problems: 53, Nos. 21–24; 54, Nos.
    25–28
systems of equations, types of, 49
  related problems: 53, Nos. 13–20

temperature, 40
temperature conversion, 8, 31, 54
  related problems: 4, No. 6; 10, Nos. 1–12;
    27, Nos. 2, 3; 35, No.
    2; 54, Nos. 5, 8; 77, No. 1
temperature relationship
  related problem: 43, No. 6
thermochemistry
  related problem: 16, No. 18
titration, 33
trinomial, 17

unit conversion, 19
  related problems: 16, Nos. 1–8; 21, Nos.
    1–8

vapor pressure, 41
  related problem: 54, No. 9
vapor pressure
  of solution, 26
  of water, 120
variable, 70
  related problems: 77, Nos. 1–15
voltage, calculation of
  related problems: 96, Nos. 18–20

X-ray
  related problem: 43, No. 8